EFT Level 1
Comprehensive
Training Resource

Ann Adams and Karin Davidson

Energy Psychology Press
P.O. Box 442, Fulton, CA 95439
www.energypsychologypress.com
Cataloging-in-Publication Data

This book demonstrates an impressive personal improvement tool. It is not a substitute for training in psychology or psychotherapy. Nothing contained herein is meant to replace qualified medical advice. The authors urge the reader to use these techniques under the supervision of a qualified therapist or physician. The authors and publisher do not assume responsibility for how the reader chooses to apply the techniques herein.

Cover design by Victoria Valentine
Editing by Stephanie Marohn
Illustrations by Kari Reed www.ArtbyKariReed.com
Typesetting by HowToTap.com
Printed in USA
First Edition

10 9 8 7 6 5 4 3 2 1

Disclaimer

Please read the following before proceeding:

The information presented in this training resource entitled EFT–Emotional Freedom Techniques (the "Training Resource"), including ideas, suggestions, techniques, and other materials, is educational in nature and is provided only as general information. The information presented in the Training Resource is not intended to create and does not constitute any professional relationship between the reader and the authors and should not be relied upon as medical, psychological, coaching, or other professional advice of any kind or nature whatsoever.

This Training Resource contains information regarding an innovative meridian-based healing technique called Emotional Freedom Techniques (EFT). EFT uses the ancient Chinese meridian system with a gentle tapping procedure that stimulates designated meridian end points on the face and body. Although EFT appears to have promising mental, spiritual, and physical benefits, it has yet to be fully researched by the Western academic, medical, and psychological communities and, therefore, is considered experimental. EFT is self-regulated and is considered "alternative" or "complementary" to the healing arts that are licensed in the United States.

Due to the experimental nature of EFT, that it is a relatively new healing approach, and because the extent of EFT's effectiveness, risks, and benefits are not fully known, you agree to assume and accept full responsibility for any and all risks associated with reading this Training Resource and using EFT. You understand that if you choose to use EFT, it is possible that emotional or physical sensations or additional unresolved memories may surface, which could be perceived as negative side effects. Emotional material may continue to surface after using EFT, indicating that other issues may need to be addressed. Previously vivid or traumatic memories may fade, which could adversely impact your ability to provide detailed legal testimony regarding a traumatic incident.

EFT is not a substitute for medical or psychological treatment. You agree to consult with your professional health-care provider for any specific medical problem or psychological disorder. In addition, you understand that any information contained in this Training Resource is not to be considered a recommendation that you stop seeing any of your health-care professionals or taking any prescribed medication, without consulting your health-care professional, even if, after reading this Training Resource and using EFT, it appears and indicates that such medication or therapy is unnecessary. The authors strongly advise that you seek professional advice as appropriate before using EFT, before implementing any protocol or opinion expressed in this Training Resource, and before making any health decision.

If you intend to use EFT with others, you agree to use EFT only within your prescribed scope of practice, under appropriate ethical guidelines, and to comply with all applicable laws and regulations. Any stories or testimonials contained herein do not constitute a warranty, guarantee, or prediction regarding the outcome of an individual using EFT for any particular issue. Further, you understand the authors make no warranty, guarantee, or prediction regarding any outcome from you using EFT for any particular issue. While all materials and links to other resources are posted in good faith, the accuracy, validity, effectiveness, completeness, or usefulness of any information herein, as with any publication, cannot be guaranteed. The authors accept no responsibility or liability whatsoever for the use or misuse of the information provided here, including the use of information in links to other resources.

By continuing to read this Training Resource you agree to fully release, indemnify, and hold harmless, the authors, their respective heirs, personal representatives, agents, consultants, employees, and assigns from any claim or liability whatsoever and for any damage or injury, personal, financial, emotional, psychological, or otherwise that you may incur, arising at any time out of, or in relation to, your use of the information presented in this Training Resource. If any court of law rules that any part of the Disclaimer is invalid, the Disclaimer stands as if those parts were struck out.

By Continuing to Read the Training Resource
You Agree to All of the Above

Note: This training resource is the culmination of input from dozens of experienced trainers of EFT. The authors have remained faithful to Gary Craig's "official EFT" and attempted to cover all level 1 EFT topics in an informative and helpful way. Although you can learn EFT from this training resource, it is not intended to be a stand-alone training resource. Its intent is to complement live training by going into more depth about the use of EFT than any one class can do in the time allotted.

This training resource is written as a reference resource for all serious students of EFT. It is meant as a companion for review after watching DVDs and as reinforcement and review for any level 1 EFT class. It can also be used as a training resource for EFT exercises.

Though actual client cases have been used, names and other identifying information have been changed.

Contents

EFT METHODS

EFT FOR PHYSICAL ISSUES

BIBLIOGRAPHY

APPENDIX A – EFT WORKSHOP EXERCISES

APPENDIX B – POWERFUL EFT QUESTIONS

APPENDIX C – ANSWERS TO "TEST YOUR KNOWLEDGE"

Note from the Authors

Ann Adams: Skeptical? I was. Healthy skepticism, when introduced to any process outside the typical practice, is normal. I sat in my introduction to EFT class at an NASW-GA Conference in 1999. I was incredulous – tapping on points of the body to relieve emotional and physical pain seemed a bit, well, out there! I had been a no-nonsense manager in the mental health system for over thirty-four years. I was focused on the effectiveness and efficiency of our staff and the methods they used. I expected proven methods to be utilized for our clients. But I'd always been puzzled as to why someone can be traumatized in the blink of an eye, but the trauma seems to last forever. Why can't someone become un-traumatized as quickly as it happened or, at least, in some reasonable length of time similar to healing from a broken leg? If what the workshop leader, Dr. Jane Holmes, was telling the class about EFT was true, there was a way to resolve trauma and almost as quickly as when it happened. I was so fascinated I had to learn more. Though nothing works for absolutely everyone, my experience showed me that EFT could be used effectively for a variety of situations. I was hooked.

Karin Davidson: I had watched some of Gary Craig's DVDs and started trying it out. It worked so well and so easily that I wanted to use my TV production background to help spread this amazing technique. I was able to connect with Ann Adams just as she was organizing EFT Master Showcases around the world. I videotaped them all. I watched "miracle" after "miracle" from behind my camera. It seemed impossible, but the results were very real. I didn't care how weird it was – it worked! In twenty minutes, a very angry woman who had been blaming men for the cause of every terrible event in the history of humankind walked up to the closest man in the audience and hugged him, apologizing. A woman with a twenty-year-old knee pain having to use crutches walked off the stage unaided. The emotional scars of rape, gone. Fear of public speaking, gone. The pain of losing a loved one, replaced with tender memories. All these people healed. I interviewed many of the subjects, and the results that occurred on stage remained years later. All the emotional issues and physical problems that were resolved remained resolved. I videotaped and edited more than one hundred sessions and trainings by thirty of the top EFTers in the world. I began by wanting to help EFT and ended up getting the best training anyone could ask for. I am forever grateful.

Introduction to EFT

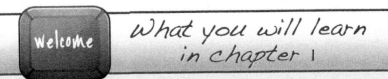

What you will learn in chapter 1

The origins and development of EFT

Six basics of energy psychology

Bridges to understanding EFT

After twenty years working as a traditionally trained psychotherapist, I discovered meridian tapping and it revolutionized my practice. I could now accomplish things for my clients that I had never been able to even approximate before.

— DR. PATRICIA CARRINGTON, PhD

Emotional Freedom Techniques (EFT) is a collection of self-help techniques that address the mind-body connection. These techniques involve acupressure and mental-emotional focus. Fundamentally, one taps lightly or touches specific points on the body's energy pathways (called meridians) while focusing on an event or emotion. And although EFT works perfectly well by itself, it can also be combined with other therapies. Increasingly, counselors and therapists are using these techniques in their psychotherapy sessions.

There is increasing evidence that emotional trauma contributes greatly to disease, as demonstrated in research by professionals such as Robert Scaer, MD (2001), Lawrence LeShan, PhD, Richard E. Worthington, PhD (1956), Claus Bahne Bahnson, PhD (1980, 1981), Peter Levine, PhD (1997), Vincent Felitti, MD, and colleagues (1998), and the collective work of Hurse, Jenkins, and Rose

(1976). Thousands of individual reports have shown that EFT is able to reduce rapidly the negative emotional impact of memories and past incidents that trigger emotional and physical distress. Once the distress is reduced, removed, or reframed, the body can often rebalance itself and accelerate healing. This can be achieved through self-help EFT methods and through EFT facilitators educated in guiding this releasing process with others.

Using EFT, a person is able to reduce the negative impact of memories and past events, thereby reducing physical and emotional pain. Once the pain is reduced or removed, the body can often rebalance itself.

EFT often works where nothing else will.

EFT uses no drugs or equipment.

EFT is safe and painless.

EFT is usually rapid, long lasting, and gentle.

EFT can be easily learned by anyone, even children.

EFT can be easily self-applied.

EFT can be used at any time, anywhere.

And, you don't have to believe in EFT for it to work.

If you stimulate particular areas on the body where meridians (the body's energy pathways) are closest to the surface while focusing your mind on a negative event, the tapping can balance the negative reaction. Many times this happens in just a few minutes, and the results are often permanent. This, of course, is a simplified explanation. There are many variables that arise when you begin to work with actual emotional, physical, and psychological issues. This training resource will explain this technique and its use and will begin to explore the many concepts that enhance the efficacy of EFT.

Though many important EFT research questions remain to be answered, a great deal of groundwork is already in place. EFT has been researched in more than seven countries, by more than fifty investigators. Their results have been published in more than fifteen peer-reviewed journals, including top-tier journals such as the Journal of Clinical Psychology and the flagship APA journal Psychotherapy: Theory, Research, Practice, Training. EFT researchers include investigators affiliated with many different institutions:

Harvard Medical School (USA)

University of California at Berkeley (USA)

City University of New York (USA)

Walter Reed Army Medical Center (USUHS) (USA)

Texas A&M University (USA)

Lund University (Sweden)

Ankara University (Turkey)

Santo Tomas University (Philippines)

Lister Hospital (England)

César Vallejo University (Peru)

Griffith University (Australia)

EFT has been explored and demonstrated to be an effective energy psychology technique in many studies and writings (Arenson 2001; Baker, Carrington, and Putilin 2009; Brattberg 2008; Callahan 1985; Durlacher 1994; Flint 1999; Gallo 2002; Hover-Kramer 2002; Lake and Wells 2003; Lambrou and Pratt 2000; Rowe 2005; and Wells and colleagues 2003).

Although EFT should still be considered an experimental technique, there are many testimonials and anecdotal reports showing that EFT has been used successfully for a variety of purposes, including:

- Fears related to public speaking, performance, concentration, sports, and tests
- Phobias, e.g., the fear of spiders, heights, flying, enclosed spaces, and success
- Trauma, PTSD, emotional effects from physical abuse
- Depression, anger, and other negative emotions
- Addictions, e.g., to alcohol and other substances, smoking, eating, Internet, and pornography
- Insomnia and other sleeping issues
- Physical conditions and disease

Gary Craig, the developer of EFT, created DVD sets that demonstrated its use. In his video set *From EFT to the Palace of Possibilities: Foundational EFT* Disk 1 at the time locator of 9:30 minutes to 22:15, Craig shows edited (before and after) versions of some actual case studies:

- Using EFT for fear of mice and rats – the woman ends up petting a rat in a glass cage.
- Using EFT for cigarette cravings – the man is surprised to find he no longer wants the cigarette.
- Using EFT for childhood trauma – the woman is able to talk about the incidents without becoming upset. She is also in the audience four months later and explains that she can still talk about the incidents without becoming upset.
- Using EFT for tightness in the jaw – the woman had the tightness for three years and it was relieved with EFT. The day after using EFT she reported the tightness was still completely gone.

The Development of EFT

Before the work of Sigmund Freud, there was not a clear idea that mental or emotional suffering might be maintained by the brain. In other words, it might take more than willpower or good intentions to relieve that suffering. Freud brought this idea to the forefront with his work on the subconscious. It took later developments in cognitive neuroscience, however, to understand that the subconscious mind was more than just "thought." From the 1950s, behavioral psychologists began demonstrating how appropriate stimuli could affect behavior and that changing behavior could change neural pathways. By changing the neural pathways, thoughts, emotions, and behavior changed. In the following decades, clinicians began to put together these ideas of the mind-body connection to develop methods like Eye Movement Desensitization and Reprocessing (EMDR), Thought Field Therapy (TFT), Advanced Integrative Therapy (AIT), and Emotional Freedom Techniques (EFT) (Church, 2009).

Today, professional and international associations work to define and promote high standards of research, professional training, and practice in this area. Two well-known associations are ACEP (Association for Comprehensive Energy Psychology), which terms these methods "energy psychology" and AAMET (Association for the Advancement of Meridian Energy Techniques), which uses the term "meridian energy therapies."

While the concepts of EFT were developed from the realization that our minds affect our bodies, the mechanics of EFT evolved from the same concepts as acupuncture, which uses needles to stimulate the body along lines or pathways called "meridians." EFT combines stimulating these meridian points (with pressure, or tapping, rather than needles) while focusing on a specific issue or problem.

Acupuncture

Acupuncture was used in Eastern medicine for centuries for treatment of physical issues. Since the middle 1900s, Western medical practitioners have been increasingly accepting of the practice and benefits of acupuncture.

Acupuncture has been practiced since at least 1000 BCE, and some evidence suggests it was used much earlier. Though acupuncture is commonly thought to

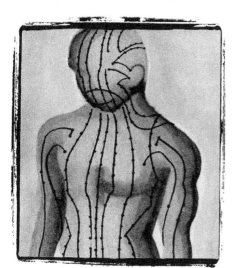

have developed in China, similar techniques have been found in many parts of the world. In the late twentieth century, several tattooed mummies were discovered in Siberia, Peru, and Chile. The oldest of these, The Tyrolian Iceman (spelled Tyrolean by other sources), was marked with fifteen groups of tattoos, which were later identified as being related to modern acupuncture points used to treat arthrosis and abdominal problems. Radiological studies and other methods found that the man suffered from arthritis in his hip, knee, and ankle joints, as well as his lumbar spine (Dorfer 1999).

Treatment of meridians was first described in *The Yellow Emperor's Classic of Medicine,* written in China sometime between 475 and 221 BCE. Two other works written in China with detailed descriptions helped to expand knowledge of the technique. The first, written around 400 CE, was a twenty-four-volume set called *A Classic of Acupuncture and Moxibustion.* The other, written between 960 and 1368 CE, was titled *The Illustrated Manual on the Points for Acupuncture and Moxibustion.* (Moxibustion refers to warming an acupoint by burning an herb, *Artemisia japonica* or mugwort, just above the skin at the site of the point.) The author of *The Illustrated Manual* also cast two life-sized bronze figures showing the meridians and points.

The Infinity Healing Center of Wisconsin explains acupuncture in a way that is very useful for our purposes: "The ancient Chinese believed that there is a universal life energy called *Chi* or *Qi* present in every living creature. This energy is said to circulate throughout the body along specific pathways that are called meridians. As long as this energy flows freely throughout the meridians, health is maintained, but once the flow of energy is blocked, the system is disrupted and pain and illness occur. Acupuncture therefore works to 'reprogram' and restore normal functions by stimulating certain points on the meridians in order to free up the Chi energy." These disruptions along the meridians can be unblocked with EFT allowing the energy to flow freely and bring emotional, as well as physical, benefits.

Applied Kinesiology

An American chiropractor, Dr. George Goodheart, was introduced to acupuncture in 1962 through a book written by the president of the Acupuncture Society in Britain. He studied it, believing that the information could be adapted to his own practice. Goodheart discovered he could use manual pressure or tapping on the acupuncture points to treat physical conditions successfully without needles.

Goodheart used the manual muscle testing he'd learned from physical therapy practice (Kendell and Kendell 1949) to determine which area of the body to treat. Seeing that emotions could be a factor in physical problems, Goodheart discovered he could use neurovascular reflexes, located at the frontal eminence on the forehead, to treat emotional factors. He referred to this process as the emotional stress release (ESR) procedure. He called his method "Applied Kinesiology" and began teaching other chiropractors this technique.

Behavioral Kinesiology

John Diamond, an Australian psychiatrist, was interested in complementary and preventative medicine. Diamond took a class from Goodheart in the 1970s. Diamond integrated his psychoanalytic training with utilizing acupuncture meridians to treat psychological problems – the beginning of meridian-based therapies as we know them. Diamond used muscle testing to determine what to treat and called his method "Behavioral Kinesiology." He used a variety of methods to treat emotional issues including positive affirmations, music, sounds, gestures, postural adjustments, nutritional supplements, and flower essences.

Diamond found that, in some cases, the result of muscle testing was "reversed" and none of his approaches were effective. He called this phenomenon a "reversal of the body morality." His patients would muscle test positive for a negative statement, such as "I want to be sick," and negative for a positive statement, such as "I want to be well" (Diamond 1988).

American psychologist Dr. Roger Callahan, who specialized in anxiety disorders, learned about Applied Kinesiology from a psychiatrist friend, Harvey Ross, who also trained with Dr. Goodheart. Callahan then took a hundred-hour course in Applied Kinesiology from chiropractors David Walther and Robert Blaich (Gallo 2002).

Like Diamond, Callahan saw the potential of Applied Kinesiology for emotional and mental health issues. He began to elaborate on the work of Goodheart and Diamond, developing what he named "Callahan Techniques," which is commonly referred to as "Thought Field Therapy" (TFT). In the Callahan Techniques, the client tunes into the issue as the therapist manually muscle tests the client. Muscle testing is a diagnostic method and the results are used to find the order of the points requiring tapping. After testing, the therapist taps on the points in the order diagnosed. Callahan believes the exact order of the points creates an individual code for each client.

After tapping the diagnosed points, the therapist then rechecks with manual muscle testing. If necessary, the therapist repeats the procedure until the client's muscle tests strong while thinking about the issue. Callahan, like Diamond, found that there were people who suffered from reversed muscle testing results that blocked effectiveness. He called this phenomenon "psychological reversal" and developed procedures to deal with such reversals.

Callahan began experimenting with his new technique on his clients. One of his clients, Mary, suffered from a long-term, severe fear of water. One day, while they were working on this fear in his office, Mary mentioned for the first time that her fearful feeling was located in her stomach. Callahan decided to try having her tap on the end point of the stomach meridian (located under the eye). He hoped that the tapping would relieve some of her stomach symptoms. To his great surprise, after tapping under her eye, she said her fear of water was gone, jumped up, and ran to the pool outside his office.

With this success, Callahan was encouraged to continue developing his techniques. As he gained experience, he noted that similar emotional issues appeared to share similar patterns of points that were consistently diagnosed as needing tapping. He identified various algorithms (a specific series of tapping points) for specific issues.

As he practiced, he began to find that this new tapping method, though not always as simple and successful as in Mary's story, was more effective than traditional therapy. He used muscle testing to discover which points needed to be stimulated for each individual and created the system of Thought Field Therapy (TFT), using muscle testing and tapping points. Callahan then began teaching his system to other professionals.

Callahan originally used affirmative statements such as, "Even though I have X problem, I deeply and completely accept myself," as his clients tapped. Later, Callahan dropped all such affirmative statements, having his clients simply tune in to their issue as they tapped. He felt it was the percussion on the points that resolved the issues, not any statements made, positive or otherwise.

Callahan's students went in a variety of directions, developing various refinements and advancements. Some of these modified energy techniques have copyright restrictions. Some require extensive and often expensive training. One of these variations, EFT, developed by Gary Craig, is simple and inexpensive, and the basics can be learned quickly and by anyone.

The Birth of Energy Psychology

Since Goodheart, Diamond, and Callahan, many others have developed methods utilizing various meridian points. Psychologist Fred Gallo coined the term "energy psychology" as a generic term to describe the growing number of tapping methods working with this energy flow. Gallo was one of Callahan's students who went on to develop a method called Energy Diagnosis and Treatment (EDxTM).

Another psychologist, Dr. Patricia Carrington, learned of these techniques and developed her own single-algorithm tapping method, ACUTAP, in 1988 (Gallo 2000).

Gary Craig developed EFT in the mid 1990s. More than thirty variations appeared in the 1990s, using the umbrella term "energy psychology" described by Gallo in his 1998 book, *Energy Psychology*. In 1999, the Association for Comprehensive Energy Psychology (ACEP) was formed as a professional body to foster awareness and acceptance of the wide variety of energy psychology techniques.

In his self-published manual, *Getting Results*, Marcus Barker, MD (Barker 2001, 10), synthesizes six main concepts of energy psychology:

1. The body "remembers" all its experiences in life.
2. There is a vital energy that flows throughout the body. That flow can become blocked, creating a "disruption" and throwing the body out of balance.
3. Accessing and focusing on (but not reliving) an upsetting thought, issue, or event are important to treating the specific problem.
4. Having a troubling thought or problem causes a disruption that blocks the natural flow of energy.
5. This blocked energy can be "reversed" at some point along the meridian. This reversal, which can be corrected, can slow or stop progress.
6. Through a step-by-step procedure involving tapping on acupuncture points, an issue can be resolved or modified.

The Birth of Emotional Freedom Techniques (EFT)

Gary Craig, also a student of Callahan, streamlined and simplified TFT with a single-algorithm method (EFT). Craig had a lifelong interest in how our thoughts influence our reality, and he studied many self-help methods, including Neuro-Linguistic Programming (NLP), whose language and reframing patterns later influenced Craig's development of EFT.

Two psychologists, Richard Bandler and John Grinder, developed NLP in the United States in the early 1970s (Bandler and Grinder 1975a, b). They studied the thinking and behavioral skills used by particularly effective and successful therapists such as Milton Erickson, Fritz Pearls, and Virginia Satir.

Bandler and Grinder broke down the actions of these successful therapists into teachable pieces so that the skills and behaviors could be duplicated. Craig became a master NLP practitioner, and NLP language patterns can be seen in the language used by Craig in his utilization of EFT.

In the mid 1990s, Craig started a website, emofree.com (the site is no longer active), and an e-mail dialogue with therapists, counselors, and other facilitators around the world in an attempt to spread EFT. By his retirement in June 2010, more than one million people from all over the world had downloaded his free instructional manual. Therapists, facilitators, and self-helpers all around the globe now practice EFT.

What Is EFT?

EFT involves tapping on acupressure points while focusing on a particular emotion, physical sensation, or event. We tap as we focus to release negative emotion(s) resulting from events in our past.

As we travel through life, we assign meaning to the events that occur to and around us. When you have a negative experience as a child, for example, your mother yelled at you for bringing mud in the house, you form an association in your mind between the event and the negative impact it had on you at the time. Your emotional reaction is tied to the memory of the event.

Part of our unconscious has the job of keeping us safe and is constantly looking for threats to our well-being. It is constantly comparing our current circumstances to these negative memories of the past. If something happens now that is identified in any way as similar to a prior experience, in which we learned to respond in a particular way, that information can be utilized to guide our reaction to the current event.

One part of the limbic system, the hippocampus, appears to be required for the formation of long-term memory. It has an interesting function that relates to the emotional content of memory. The hippocampus is responsible for categorizing information, deciding what's important enough for long-term storage. The hippocampus "helps organize retrieval systems for the information by cross-associating and 'contextualizing' the information with flags such as scents, emotions, and images" (Milne 1995). In other words, the flags distinguish important items from unimportant ones. The limbic system attaches emotional flags to certain memories to warn us of potential danger.

These interpretations can be useful in reminding us to exercise caution. Touching any hot stove can burn you. Some cats will scratch you. Some dogs bite. Not all people in the world can be trusted. This same protective system can become problematic if you generalize one, or several, negative experiences to a broader meaning. If a cat scratched you or scared you in some way, this negative event could be generalized to a fear of all cats. If your parents regularly expected more from you than you could give at a young age, you may interpret this to mean that, even as an adult, you are not a capable person. You might then use your generalized negative interpretation of an event to give the same meaning to any event you interpret as similar: fear of all dogs or cats or people. Or that, since you couldn't do things to meet your parents' expectations, you can never do anything well. Similar events can trigger your old negative and unproductive interpretation of yourself and the world.

We use EFT to focus on the specific event in which
we learned the problematic or negative interpretation
of self and/or the world.

Building Bridges

EFT can seem unconventional: one taps on acupressure points while talking about an issue to relieve emotional and physical discomfort. Because of EFT's unconventional nature, it is helpful to develop a connection between EFT and concepts people currently understand. Founder Gary Craig called this link to the familiar "building a bridge to understanding," which helps create rapport with the reader or audience and acceptance of EFT. Offering a "bridge" linking EFT to familiar concepts is important to remember when attempting to tell others about EFT.

Gary Craig offered these bridges:
- EFT is like hypnotherapy but adds extra power to the process because it integrates the body's subtle energies and it integrates beautifully with hypnotherapy because it allows us to take the process even deeper.
- EFT is like talk therapy with the advantage that it allows us to get to the issues faster and resolve them more thoroughly.
- EFT enhances massage therapy by adding an important emotional relaxation process.
- EFT blends perfectly with cognitive behavioral therapy because it helps bring up the issues faster and creates more (and deeper) cognitive shifts behind the scenes.
- EFT is like systematic desensitization except that it is much gentler and often faster.
- EFT enhances chiropractic work by allowing the inclusion of important emotional issues and the integration of the body's subtle energies.

It is helpful to modify these examples as needed to fit your audience.

John Freedom, CEHP, EFT Trainer and ACEP Research Coordinator, creates a wonderful bridge when he tells his classes:

EFT is a technique for *behavioral desensitization*. Does the name "Ivan Pavlov" ring a bell? Pavlov was a Russian psychologist and founder of the behaviorist school of psychology. He is probably most famous for a series of experiments in which he rang a bell as he gave meat to his dogs. The dogs very rapidly learned to associate the smell of meat with the sound of the bell, and would then salivate whenever they heard a bell.

What many people forget is that *we are all Pavlovian dogs*. Behavioral conditioning is based on associative learning. If a white cat jumps on and startles a little girl when she is a baby, she may then associate cats with feeling startled; and may then feel slightly anxious whenever she encounters anything white or furry.

Associative conditioned learning is not all "negative." As children, we learn to associate the sound of rustling skirts with Mom, greasy work clothes with Dad, the smell of fresh baked bread with Grandma. Thereafter, whenever we hear, see, or smell anything similar to these (repetitive, conditioned) memories, we will reexperience these same feelings and sensations, automatically, mechanically, and often unconsciously.

Tapping on meridian points desensitizes these conditioned responses and reassociates (i.e., counter-conditions) a "relaxation response" with the formerly stressful stimulus.

The relaxation response is an innate, autonomic response, parallel to the fight or flight response, except that it slows us down and moves us into "rest and rejuvenate" mode, rather than fight or flight. This response was discovered by Dr. Herbert Benson at Harvard University. (Personal Correspondence, October 25, 2010.)

Test Your Knowledge

1. True or false? Children cannot be taught EFT.

2. EFT can be performed by

    a. only acupuncturists.

    b. only psychologists.

    c. anyone who is willing to learn it.

    d. only those who have studied all of founder Gary Craig's training DVDs.

3. What "bridge" would you use to describe EFT?

Answers can be found in Appendix C

The Discovery Statement

The Discovery Statement
"The cause of all negative emotions is a disruption
in the body's energy system."

Gary Craig described the Discovery Statement as the essence of EFT:
Negative thought -> creates energy disruption -> creates the negative emotion

Here is an example of how our thoughts can affect how we feel and react. A group of people visit the Grand Canyon. As they stand at the guardrail to view the scene:

- Many people think immediately of the immense beauty of it all and are touched and impressed; they feel gratitude and awe.
- Others only think of their vulnerability and immediately feel afraid of the height at which they are standing.
- Others only respond to the huge openness, feel overwhelmed and retreat to their cars for "safety."
- Others think of some event from their past that involved height, something larger than themselves, open spaces, groups of people, or guardrails; they have a negative emotion or uncomfortable physical feeling that upsets them.
- Others are impressed by the beauty but immediately think of someone they lost with whom they would like to have shared the moment, and they become sad.

Not all have the same level of upset. Some responses are mild, some are moderate, and some people feel such a negative response they have to leave the scene immediately. The point here is that no two people have the same reaction to the same exact event. The people enjoying the beauty are fine. Those with negative thoughts about any part of viewing the Grand Canyon experience an energy disruption, which causes the physical or emotional discomfort. Your internal response to any situation is determined by your past experiences.

The Discovery Statement says that negative emotions are caused by an energy disruption. Energy disruptions happen when we have a negative thought. This disruption can be seen as a "clog" in our energy system. We clear the clog by tapping on the meridian points while focusing on the bothersome issue. Tapping sends pulsing through the meridian and therein "fixes" the energy disruption. Energy flows freely again and the negative emotion is neutralized.

Tapping while focusing on the negative emotion clears the disruption. The disruption is described in TFT (Thought Field Therapy) as a "perturbation," or disturbance, in the thought field.

According to the concept in TFT, each of our thoughts is contained in a "thought field." It is the perturbation or disturbance in this thought field that is addressed in TFT by tapping. The perturbation in the thought field contains active information that triggers the neurological, chemical, hormonal, and cognitive changes in the person. These changes result in the experience of negative emotions. These perturbations exert their influence by causing imbalances in the body's energy system. In other words, disturbances in the thought field cause an imbalance in the body's energy system that results in negative emotions.

Most people believe that the upsetting event or trauma in their lives is what causes their related negative emotions. EFT and other energy techniques recognize a different causative factor. The event does not cause the emotional upset.

> The *thought* about the event causes the energy disruption
> that, in turn, causes the negative emotion.

When the energy disruption is balanced using EFT, the emotions around the memory are released. When working with traumatic events using energy psychology, the person does not need to talk about or relive all the gory details; being tuned in to the issue as he or she taps is all that is necessary to balance the disruption.

Disruptions and Reactions

When our energy is flowing smoothly, we feel calm and peaceful. Conversely, when this energy is disrupted, we become out of balance and overly emotional. This disruption, or blockage, limits our ability to function at our best. In their book *Emotional Healing in Minutes*, Paul and Valerie Lynch liken this to boulders in a stream; the energy is ??? ??? flowing freely. Removing our personal boulders allows balance and equi??? to return.

When water flowing in a stream reaches a boulder, the water flow is disrupted. When something happens now that triggers a past response, our subconscious mind looks to the past for a way to react. It then reacts according to that past disruption, and the flow of energy is disrupted again.

Any stimulus can trigger a disruption: sounds, smells, sights, tastes, objects, animals, certain environments, even just a triggering word or phrase.

The subconscious mind reacts according to specific, earlier learned "rules of behavior" *even when those rules are out of date.*

What EFT Does

There is a growing body of research pointing to the efficacy of EFT. It is not the purpose of this training resource to describe this research in detail. Several websites, however, track ongoing research, published papers, and articles proposing why energy psychology techniques such as EFT work. A comprehensive list of research, articles, and papers can be found at *energypsych.org* and *eftuniverse.com*.

The first study of EFT published in a peer-reviewed journal was done by a research team led by Steve Wells, an Australian psychologist. The team studied the effect of EFT on phobias of small animals and insects by comparing it with the effect of a deep breathing technique on the same phobias. While each of the groups improved, the EFT participants improved significantly more than did the deep breathing group on four out of the five subjective and behavioral measures.

On the single physiological measure used – pulse rate – both conditions showed a significant decrease, but there was no difference between the two treatments. On the behavioral test – measuring how close the person dared to walk toward their feared animal before and then after whichever treatment they were given – the EFT participants held their gains far better than did the deep breathing subjects when the groups were reassessed six to nine months after they had learned their technique.

In other words, the findings suggest that "a single treatment session using EFT to reduce specific phobias can produce valid behavioral and subjective effects" (Wells 2003). In other words, the findings suggest that those people who act less fearful right after learning EFT, with respect to a feared object, continue to act less fearful of that animal even after a long passage of time during which they have not used EFT.

The Wells study was later replicated by Harvey Baker of Queens University in New York (Baker & Siegel 2010). In this study, "EFT was compared to a supportive interview. There was no significant difference in expectation of help before treatment between these two conditions and the finding that EFT produced significantly greater decrease in fear whereas the interview did not help at all held up even after statistically controlling for expectations" (Baker 2009, 44).

A similar study explored EFT alone and in combination with diaphragmatic breathing and found similar lasting effects for EFT in phobias other than fear of small animals (Salas, Brooks, & Rowe 2011).

Exciting research in neuroscience has begun to postulate that memory, even long-term memory, is *not* static. The work of Karim Nader (2009) shows that memory, once recalled, must actually reform or "reconsolidate." This means that every time we access a memory, it is rewritten. His research focuses on interrupting the reconsolidation of the memory. This supports the idea that EFT works to break the connection between the cognition of a memory and any negative emotion associated with it.

Author of *Psychoanalytic Energy Psychotherapy: Inspired by Thought Field Therapy, EFT, TAT, and Seemorg Matrix*, Phil Mollon suggests that, when a memory that is emotional for us comes to mind, neuro-biological changes occur. Mollon calls upon the research showing, through MRIs, that mechanical forces such as tapping send electrochemical impulses to the limbic and cortical regions of the brain that control stress or fear, possibly sending " noise" or " disruption" that affects the conditioned emotional response to the memory.

He relates this idea to that of "neural plasticity," postulating that the memory becomes active and pliable, susceptible to taking in new information, thus allowing an easier updating of information into the patterning of emotional response to the memory.

The following are six papers (worth reading if you are a serious inquirer) that suggest what could be happening in the body during tapping. They discuss the neurological, epigenetic, psychoneuroimmunological, and hormonal pathways believed to be active during EFT sessions:

- "Rapid Treatment of PTSD: Why Psychological Exposure with Acupoint Tapping May Be Effective," David Feinstein, PhD, *Psychotherapy: Theory, Research, Practice, Training* (2010)
- "The Neurochemistry of Counterconditioning: Acupressure Desensitization in Psychotherapy," James Lane, PhD, *Energy Psychology: Theory, Research, and Treatment* (2009)
- "The Dream to Freedom Technique, a Methodology for Integrating the Complementary Therapies of Energy Psychology and Dreamwork," Robert J. Hoss and Lynne M. Hoss, DreamScience Foundation, *Energy Psychology: Theory, Research, and Treatment* (2010)
- "Modulating Gene Expression through Psychotherapy: The Contribution of Non-Invasive Somatic Interventions," David Feinstein and Dawson

Church, *Review of General Psychology*, American Psychological Association Journal (2010)

- "Energy Psychology in Rehabilitation: Origins, Clinical Applications, and Theory," Fred Gallo PhD, *Energy Psychology Journal* (2009)
- "Why Tapping Works: A Sense for Healing, Speculations from an Observable Brain," Ronald A. Ruden, MD, PhD, *HealingTheMind.net* (2005)

Test Your Knowledge

1. What is the "Discovery Statement?"

2. EFT holds that a person's_____ cause(s) negative emotions.

> *a. biology*
>
> *b. negative experiences*
>
> *c. thoughts about negative experiences*
>
> *d. negative friends*

3. True or false? Generally speaking, EFT tends to work slower than traditional therapy.

4. True or false? When something happens now, our subconscious minds look in the past for a way to react.

Answers can be found in Appendix C

Using EFT

What you will learn in chapter 2

How to perform EFT (the "Basic Recipe")

The tapping points

The importance of "getting specific"

How to Tap

The points used in EFT are familiar. We use them in common everyday ways, many times without realizing we are actually using acupressure points:

- Massaging under eyes
- Massaging temples
- Palm or fist to chest
- Hand on chest when startled
- Palm to forehead
- Heel of hand to forehead
- Folding arms
- Holding face in hands
- Biting on fingernails or fingers
- Scratching head
- Wringing hands
- Patting a child on the head

The points used in EFT are either the end point or close to the end point on each of the twelve main meridians and two additional meridians called the Conception Vessel and the Governing Vessel. These fourteen meridians are lines

26

of energy running through our body. The twelve primary meridians, six yin meridians and six yang meridians, are each associated with specific organs in the body. The other two are not associated with organs; rather, they strengthen the connections among the other meridians. The Governing Vessel runs roughly up the spine from just above the anus over the head and ends just above the upper lip. It meets all the yang meridians. The Conception Vessel runs up the front of the body from just in front of the anus to the groove just below the lower lip and meets the yin meridians.

Note: One other point on the crown of the head, though not a part of the initial EFT Basic Recipe, was generally used by Gary Craig in the later years during his demonstrations.

Along these meridian lines of energy are more than five hundred points used by acupuncturists. Tapping, pressing, or holding some of these points while focusing on the problem appears to enable a release that reduces or eliminates physical or emotional pain.

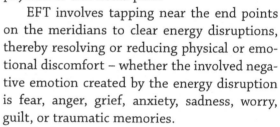

EFT involves tapping near the end points on the meridians to clear energy disruptions, thereby resolving or reducing physical or emotional discomfort – whether the involved negative emotion created by the energy disruption is fear, anger, grief, anxiety, sadness, worry, guilt, or traumatic memories.

The basics of EFT are simple. In a very short time, you can learn the tapping points and wording and begin applying them to your life and your issues with reasonable success. The art and skill of using EFT for situations in which EFT is working slowly, or appears not to work at all, takes longer. This training resource will teach the basics. To become truly proficient requires additional training and extensive practice.

The EFT Basic Recipe – "Shortcut" Method

The "Basic Recipe" consists of tapping on seven meridian points instead of all fourteen. In earlier versions of Gary Craig's introductory *EFT Manual*, the term "Basic Recipe" referred to the use of all fourteen meridian points. In *The EFT Manual, Second Edition*, the shorter (seven point) version of the "recipe," previously referred to as "The Shortcut," is referred to as the Basic Recipe. Tapping using all fourteen meridian points is now called the "Full Basic Recipe." The EFT Basic Recipe, formerly the "Shortcut," is the most commonly used tapping sequence. Gary Craig first formulated the longer tapping sequence but found that tapping on the seven points was almost always as effective as tapping on fourteen points. Additional points, or the entire long form of EFT, can be used when the shorter Basic Recipe is not effective. The "Full Basic Recipe" with its additional points and sequence variations will be detailed in chapter 7, but, currently, this shorter sequence is the most widely used by Craig and most EFT practitioners.

EFT involves tapping about seven times on each meridian point with the tips of two fingers (the index and middle finger), then moving on to tap the next point. *You can tap more than 7 times on any one point if you feel a more emotional or sensual shift in using that one point longer.*

You can tap with either hand on either side of your body. You can switch sides in tapping – first the left point then a right point. Many people like to tap with both hands on both sides at the same time. Some like to tap on one point on one side then the corresponding point on the other side in a sort of rhythmic way. Other variations on tapping points include simply rubbing the points. John Diepold, Ph.D., originator of the "Touch and Breathe" method, says that you can just lightly touch each point as you take a slow deep breath, then move on to the next one.

You can use whatever tapping method feels most comfortable for you.

Here are the nine Basic Recipe points:

- **Karate Chop (KC)** point. Find the fleshy part of the outside of your hand below your little finger. This point is used for the "Setup." Many practitioners use the abbreviation SH for Side of the Hand.
- **Eyebrow (EB)** point. The beginning of the eyebrow just above your nose.
- **Side of the Eye (SE)** point. Beside your eye, just outside the eye socket close to the rim of the bone but not on the temple.
- **Under the Eye (UE)** point. On the bone, just below your pupil if you were looking straight ahead.
- **Under the Nose (UN)** point. Under your nose, right in the little groove, midway between the bottom of your nose and your top lip.
- **Chin (Ch)** point. Between your bottom lip and the bone of your chin, right in the little groove.
- **Collarbone (CB)** point. This point is actually not directly on the collarbone, but about an inch below the knobby protrusion of the collarbone (or clavicle) near the center of your body; a mirror can help you find this point. Find the "u" shape about where a man would knot a tie; go down one inch and over one inch (either side) to locate this point.

Karate Chop (KC)

Collarbone (CB)

- **Under Arm (UA)** point. On the side of your body, about four inches below your arm pit. For women, it is about where the bra band lies.
- **Top of Head (H)** point. Use all of your fingers to tap on the crown of your head. This point can be added as first in the tapping points after the Setup on the KC (side of the hand) or as the last point tapped.

Under Arm (UA)

Test Your Knowledge

1. The Karate Chop point is located:

   a. near the elbow.

   b. on the fleshy side of the hand below the little finger.

   c. at the base of the heel.

   d. under the eye.

2. Where are the other "Basic Recipe" points located on the body?

3. True or false? You must tap using the fingers of your dominant hand.

Answers can be found in Appendix C

The EFT Process – Where to Begin

There are several steps to resolving issues using EFT:

1. Choose a specific emotion or physical discomfort (or a memory, problem, or event) to address. This is often first described as "the time when." For tapping to be most effective, the "problem," your time when, or event, should be specifically stated. (More details follow on how to develop a specific statement.)

2. Test the intensity of how much the emotion/physical discomfort/issue/ problem/event bothers you *currently* on some kind of scale, generally a 0-to-10 scale (0 being not bothersome).

3. Create a name for your issue. We'll call it [the event] by this name for simplicity. This name will be used as a Reminder Phrase to say as you tap the points.

4. The Setup: before tapping other points, you develop a "Setup." A Setup contains two parts: a statement of [this event] *and* a statement of acceptance of self even though you have the problem. Tap on the Karate Chop (side of the hand) point and say out loud, "Even though I have [this event], I deeply and completely accept myself." Repeat this statement three times. Remember to replace [this event] with your created name for your situation.

5. The Tapping Sequence: Tap on the rest of the meridian points as listed in the earlier description while saying your Reminder Phrase: [this event].

6. Retest the intensity of the problem. Generally, the number will be lower. If your number is lower, but not down to 0, repeat the Setup again. However, this time you will modify the statement to reflect that there is still some problem around [this event]. Tap on the Karate Chop point while saying, "Even though I *still* have some of [this event], I deeply and completely accept myself." (Do this three times.)

7. Repeat the Tapping Sequence: Tap on each point saying [this remaining event]."

8. Repeat these steps until the intensity is at 0.

Note that the EFT process as just described can be divided into four main parts:

1. The Clarification
2. The Setup
3. The Tapping
4. The Testing

Let's take each one individually.

The Clarification

Develop a specific description of your issue, preferably a specific event [the time when ...] and use the 0-to-10 scale or decide on an alternative method to assess the intensity you have right now around that event. You will check for the intensity you have *in current time,* rather than how upset you were about it when it happened.

Clarifying your *specific* problem is the first step to a successful tapping experience. When we describe a problem, we most often talk in general terms: I am depressed; I am not happy in my marriage; I don't like my job; I can't seem to get anything done; I can't find the right person; my son drives me crazy. In EFT, since it is the thought that creates the energy disruption, we have to go back to the event, *the time when* we had the thought. You want to look for specific events to address with EFT.

General descriptions of the problem could be likened to a tabletop (Cialdini 1998) and the specific events that created the thoughts that led to the problem could be the legs. Some problem tabletops have many legs. To resolve a tabletop problem with EFT, you will address and cut off one leg at a time. As you cut down some of the thickest legs, however, there is a generalization effect as these bigger legs take other smaller legs down with them. As EFT resolves some of the bigger specific events, the smaller events sometimes fall on their own.

For the best results with EFT, it is important to *be specific*. Pick one leg at a time. Getting specific involves picking a time and an event that shows *how* your general problem is a problem. Be specific about *what* happened, *when* and *where*, *who* was involved, and *how* you felt about it.

I'm depressed.	Last week, I saw my ex and got into yet another pointless fight about our divorce settlement.
I am not happy in my marriage.	Last night, Joe looked bored and walked away from me when I was telling him about my new promotion. I was so hurt because he never seems to enjoy my successes.
I don't like my job.	When I was at the office party, everyone ignored me so I felt left out. Or: My boss criticized my report in front of all the staff; I was embarrassed and angry.
I can't seem to get anything done.	I got a late notice *again* from the mortgage company. Or: Yesterday, I wandered from one thing to the other and last night felt very guilty about not finishing a project I promised my sister I'd do.
I can't find the right person.	It's been six days since John told me he'd call; I feel like there is something wrong with me.
My son drives me crazy.	Last week Jess said he'd be in at nine; he came in at midnight and then screamed at me for waiting up. I am afraid for him and me.

Each of these examples takes a more general problem and narrows it down to a more specific *when and what and how*. After you have created a specific event, *as you begin to tap, more details of the situation may come up*. As these details surface, you tap for each of them. Many times, the feeling will remind you of a similar event in the past. We'll cover this more extensively later in this training resource. Address each specific event until you are in a calm emotional space, which often brings a different perception of the issue. EFT calms you so you can think more clearly about your options and opportunities.

As a beginner, it is important to work on the more specific and simpler events as compared to complex issues. A simple event is often a specific memory: the specific time when. A simple issue is one that is/was short term and you can easily measure the intensity of the emotion or physical feeling around it. Complex issues are chronic, repeated events with multiple roots and are difficult to measure. Examples of complex, difficult-to-address issues are depression, overeating, or procrastination.

When you are working on getting specific, it is helpful to think about it like searching for a topic in Google. Search for "rejected" and you get 58,900,000 hits. Search for "my boyfriend walked out" and you find 7,220,000 entries. For the best results when using EFT, form a very specific statement that truly has only one focus. Note the difference in specificity between "I was rejected" and "George picked a fight on our wedding day, called me cold-blooded, and said he wouldn't marry me if I were the last woman on earth."

The Setup

Create a problem statement from your event that is linked to an acceptance statement. Say your Setup three times as you tap on the side of your hand (or on the Sore Spot, detailed later). For example, "Even though I have [this event], I deeply and completely accept myself."

The Setup is a statement or phrase with two parts:

1. A specific statement of your stated problem. Often this is as simple as identifying [The time when ...]
2. Your acceptance of yourself in spite of the problem.

The Setup is intended to address the possibility of a "reversal." Craig, like Goodheart, Diamond, and Callahan, found that, in some cases, tapping was ineffective. They postulated that this was due to a reversal in the energy system. Callahan and Craig found that this "reversal" could usually be corrected by tapping on the Karate Chop point while stating your [event] and adding acceptance-of-self phrasing. A "reversal" can be a psychological, subconscious, or environmental block that affects our energy flow and interferes with the efficacy of EFT. ("Reversal" or "psychological reversal," also called PR, will be addressed later in this training resource.) Even though evidence of reversal was present in a minority of cases, Craig decided it would be simpler to assume reversal in all cases and include the Setup in every tapping sequence. This eliminated the problem of "diagnosing" whether the person was reversed. Craig continued to use Callahan's method of tapping the side of the hand while saying the problem/acceptance Setup. Callahan later dropped using any Setup, as he felt it was the tapping while attuned to the issue that balanced the energy. Craig continued using the Setup, as he believed the wording (even though I have this problem + acceptance statement) was important to EFT effectiveness.

There are any number of words and ways to create a Setup. Begin by clarifying your problem statement as specifically as possible. As noted, such statements often begin with the phrase "The time when ..." For the acceptance part of the Setup, Gary Craig's default statement was "I deeply and completely accept myself." However, *any* statement of acceptance of yourself can be used.

Here are some examples of Setup phrasing:

Setup: Even though my mother slapped me when I was seven in front of my friend Sally for spilling my milk and I was so embarrassed, I deeply and completely accept myself.

Tapping sequence phrase/**Reminder Phrase**: Mommy slapped me.

Setup: Even though I wanted to sink into the floor when my teacher yelled at me in second grade for losing my homework, I'm OK anyway.

Tapping sequence phrase/**Reminder Phrase**: My teacher yelled at me.

Setup: Even though the school bully tripped me on the playground to make me miss the ball and I felt I let my team down, I deeply and completely accept myself anyway.

Tapping Sequence Phrase/**Reminder Phrase**: The bully tripped me.

Notice in these examples that the Reminder Phrase was the *name* of the event. Generally, you will pick the *name* that best represents your memory of the event. Often there can be a choice of Reminder Phrases. You would pick the most emotional of the parts (aspects) of the story: the bully tripped me, I missed the ball, I let my team down.

As a beginner, you will pick the name that best represents the event for you and use that name as you tap on each point. In level 2, you will learn ways to create more complex phrases. Notice, too, that each of the previous examples could be made even *more* specific. As you tap, more details could arise.

Where to Tap During the Setup: You have two options. The Karate Chop (KC) point, (side of the hand) is most commonly used. Alternatively, you can rub the Sore Spot. Either point sets up your energy system to allow the tapping to be effective.

The **Karate Chop (KC)** point is on the fatty side of the hand where you would hit a board in a karate chop. When Ann Adams was teaching EFT to kids in a residential treatment program, she referred to the Karate Chop point as the "friendly spot." When you shake hands, the part that your fingers touch is the fatty side of the hand (Karate Chop point) on the other person's hand. Ann described it to the kids as "The place you make friends with your problem."

The **Sore Spot**, so called because it is generally a little tender to the touch, is the site of one of many neurolymphatic reflexes throughout your body.

The Sore Spot is about where you would pin a medal or place a nametag. To find it, put your fingers in the "u" at your throat; go down a couple of inches, then across about four inches. When you find a spot that is a bit tender, use your fingers or the flat of your hand to gently rub that area on your chest. While the left side is most often used, a similar spot is on the right side as well. Some practitioners choose to massage both sides at the same time during a Setup.

Neurolymphatic reflexes were discovered by Dr. Frank Chapman, an osteopath in the 1930s. Through gentle pressing, or palpation, with the fingers, Chapman examined patients and found tender areas in the body that he believed to be the result of an increase in, and congestion of, lymph. Later, in applying this concept to meridian tapping techniques, such as EFT, it was found that massaging the Sore Spot (not tapping on it) resulted in correcting a psychological reversal or "polarity reversal."

You have a choice to use the Sore Spot or the side of the hand while saying the Setup. Which is better? In the downloaded *EFT Manual, Sixth Edition*, Gary Craig encourages people to use the Sore Spot. He says that, in his experience, the Sore Spot is a bit more effective than the side of the hand point – not a significant amount more, but enough that it may make a difference. He also says, however, that the Karate Chop point is easier to demonstrate and to use when teaching. A good guide might be to use the side of the hand as your standard and to switch to the Sore Spot if EFT seems not to be working or is working slowly.

The side of the hand and the Sore Spot are the only reversal correction points used by Craig in what he called "Official EFT." Other meridian tapping techniques use additional points and identify various other types of reversals. For more information about these approaches, see Fred Gallo's book *Energy Diagnostic and Treatment Methods*.

The Tapping

Create a Reminder Phrase to use while tapping on the points in the sequence. After tapping the points while saying your Reminder Phrase, reassess your intensity, adjust the Setup as needed, and repeat the sequence until the intensity is 0.

Tap about seven times on each point while repeating your Reminder Phrase.

EB – Beginning of Eyebrow
SE – Side of the Eye
UE – Under the Eye
UN – Under the Nose
Ch – Chin
CB – Collarbone
UA – Under Arm
H – Top of Head, or Crown Point

While the crown or head point was not originally part of the Basic Recipe, it is included here, as Gary Craig added this point fairly early in his demonstrations. Most EFT practitioners use it as well. Some practitioners use it at the beginning of an EFT "round" to keep with the "down the body" concept of the EFT process. Others end their round with the head point. Either way is fine.

The Testing

Decide on a method to test your progress as you go. There are a variety of ways you can decide to test an issue (more are described in chapter 5). The most common way to measure results is a numeric intensity scale from 0 to 10, 0 being no problem at all and 10 being the worst it could be. Measure before you begin tapping and again after using the Basic Recipe.

Joseph Wolpe established the Subjective Unit of Distress (SUD) scale in 1969. Simply stated, SUD is an intensity scale – a numbering system from 0 to 10. The purpose of using an intensity scale is to assess how much the issue bothers you at the time you are testing, what your intensity is now – not what your intensity was when the event first occurred.

Let's review the EFT Process:

- Select a specific memory, experience, or physical discomfort.
- Tune in and rate the current level of intensity using a 0-to-10 scale.
- Formulate a Setup and create a Reminder Phrase (i.e., the name of your issue).
- Tap on the Karate Chop point or rub the Sore Spot while saying three times, *"Even though I have [this event or feeling], I deeply and completely accept myself."*
- Tap through the points, using the Reminder Phrase.
- Test: Tune in and rate again.
- If not down to 0, modify Setup and tap through the points again. Test. Repeat as necessary.
- If the rating is not yet at 0, return to step 3 and repeat the sequence until down to 0. Modify the Setup: *"Even though I still have some of [this event or feeling], I deeply and completely accept myself."*

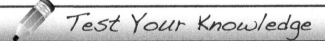

Test Your Knowledge

1. *List the four parts of the EFT process.*

2. *Describe each part of the EFT process.*

3. *The first step of the EFT process involves taking a _____ issue and making it a _____ issue.*

    a. *narrow/broad*

    b. *global/specific*

    c. *negative/positive*

4. *Briefly describe the Sore Spot.*

Answers can be found in Appendix C

Practicing the EFT Process

The Constricted Breathing exercise and Touch Your Toes exercise that follow are excellent first experiences with EFT. Most of us recognize that our breathing is affected by anxiety. Using this exercise allows us to use tapping in an apparently impersonal and nonthreatening way. We can experience EFT without focusing on our issues.

Exercise: Constricted Breathing

Let's use EFT to improve our breathing.

When we are under stress, we tend not to breathe fully and deeply. Using EFT can increase your breathing ability and, in so doing, decrease your stress. How well are you breathing right now? To assess your current quality of breath, breathe in three times slowly, gently, and as fully as you can but don't force your breath. If you have asthma, use this exercise at your own discretion.

Measure: Now assess how much of a full breath you are actually able to take. There are a variety of ways to measure success with EFT; in this case, we will use a percentage rather than a 0-to-10 scale. Give your level of breath a percentage. If you think you are already breathing fully, at 100 percent, great. Use this exercise to see if you can increase your breath up to "120 percent."

Setup: Tap on the Karate Chop point (the side of your hand) while saying, "Even though I'm not breathing to my full capacity, I deeply and

36

completely accept myself." Repeat this statement three times while tapping the side of your hand.

Tap: Tap each of the points in the EFT Basic Recipe (formerly known as the Shortcut) about seven times as you repeat at each point, "Not breathing to my full capacity."

Measure: Take a slow deep breath and assess the percentage again.

Repeat: Continue to do rounds of EFT until you reach 100 percent, your full breathing capacity. The Setup and the tapping sequence together are called "a round of EFT."

Measure: Take another gentle full breath after each round. *Don't push it.* Assess the percentage of your breath. You may notice huge improvements in your breathing with the first round or you may notice only a minimal increase. Generally, people are surprised at how much improvement is made in just one or two rounds. Others may need to tap many rounds.

In rare circumstances, breathing may not improve at all or may seem worse. This is an indication of some deeper issue regarding breathing. What came up for you as you were doing the exercise? An event, an emotion? Use EFT for whatever issue came up.

This is a very valuable exercise. When we are tense or stressed, we tend to breathe in a shallow way; we don't always notice our breathing. Try taking time to notice your breathing several times a day. Tap to take the depth of your breathing to 100 percent.

Note: At times, Gary Craig used the Constricted Breathing exercise with his clients as one of his gentle methods to decrease intensity.

Exercise: Touch Your Toes

This exercise involves carefully bending down to see how far you can reach in order to touch your toes. Create a baseline by reaching for your toes with your fingers as you gently bend down. Stand up or sit down and go through the Basic Recipe.

Use a Setup like "Even though I can only reach 'this far,' I deeply and completely accept my ability as it is." Tap each point for several rounds as you say, "Only this far." Measure by bending over again. Were you able to go farther this time?

Go slowly and don't push yourself beyond what is physically safe for you to do. Some people can already touch the floor; if that is the case for you, measure by noticing the tightness in your back or how far your elbows are bent.

3
Before You Tap

Welcome — *What you will learn in chapter 3*

The purpose of acceptance

Why we tap with the "negative"

How to measure intensity (SUD)

More about getting specific

Aspects, daisy chains, and peeling the onion

Finding the feeling in the body

The generalization effect

Acceptance

The acceptance statement is at the end of the Setup: "I deeply and completely accept myself." All Setups have the same default format:

The *problem statement* and *the acceptance of self anyway* statement.

"Even though I have/feel [...], I deeply and completely accept myself," or some similar acceptance statement.

This is the real beauty and true gift of EFT. You have a problem *and* you are still acceptable. You acknowledge the problem *and* create self-acceptance *despite* whatever the problem is.

Important: *You don't have to believe the acceptance part of the Setup. You only have to say it.* It is also helpful to say the Setup out loud with feeling and emphasis rather than just as a routine statement.

Difficulty with self-acceptance: As a beginner, it is easier to stick to the default acceptance phrase, "I deeply and completely accept myself." Some people, however, simply cannot bring themselves to say, "I accept myself." This problem can be approached as an issue in itself. "Even though I can't say I accept myself, I accept myself anyway," or "Even though I don't accept myself, I accept that is the way I feel right now." If you have difficulty in saying the default acceptance statement, it can be modified a bit. *Any* statement can be used that shows acceptance for how you truly feel.

Here are some examples of modifications for the acceptance part of the Setup:

I'm OK. (An easy one for beginners.)
I accept how I feel.
I accept some parts of myself.
I accept that I don't accept myself.
Maybe I can accept part of me someday.
I'm still a good person.
I appreciate myself.
I accept myself even though I don't.
I hope to accept myself someday.
I'm still a good/great kid. (Children respond well to this one.)

The goal is to make an acceptance statement that you can say. If necessary, modify the default, "I deeply and completely accept myself," to something you can agree to at that moment in time, even if it is, "I hope to maybe, someday, be able to think about, perhaps, deeply and completely accepting myself."

Common Question

Why are we using a "negative" statement? A common question from beginners is why the EFT process focuses on seemingly negative statements or problems. Often people are familiar with affirmations, which are positive statements of what you would like to have become your reality. An example of an affirmation would be "I am slim and trim and at my ideal, healthy weight." So why, they ask, would you want to tap for "Even though I am forty pounds overweight and feel disgusted with myself, I deeply and completely accept myself"?

The answer is simply this: You are recognizing and accepting what is going on right now for you, *your truth* at this moment in time. You are accepting how *you really feel* deep inside. You are tapping for those negative emotions around your life experiences and the negative, often limiting, beliefs that have been instilled in us all by the authorities in our lives. You are tapping for the little voice running a dialogue in your head telling you how to look at the world, how to interpret what happens, how to think about yourself, what you are and are not capable of, and so on. You are acknowledging your inner belief, even though it is negative, so you can begin the journey of full acceptance of yourself. *It is difficult or impossible to resolve problems until you have accepted that you indeed have that problem.* We spend way too much time in our lives fighting against reality. We may not like that we are forty pounds overweight, but until we accept that that is our current reality and that we are ok anyway, it is hard to begin the process of getting to our ideal weight. You don't have to *like* being overweight. You are working to *accept how you really feel* about being overweight, so that change can begin.

Gwyneth Moss, EFT Master and AAMET trainer, uses the metaphor of bandaging a wound to explain the "Why tap on the negative?" question. You want to clean out the dirt and germs first (tapping for the real issue) *before* putting on the bandage. Putting on a bandage first (tapping for a positive) would leave behind the dirt and germs (the problem), which could continue to fester and grow.

Tapping neutralizes your current negative emotions, feelings, and beliefs around whatever issue(s) you are addressing. When we tap, we tap on the deeper belief – those negative emotions/memories/fears that are holding us back from the positive thing we desire. For instance, if your actual true belief (at whatever level) is that being overweight protects you, or is the only way you can be comforted, or keeps you safe from some real or perceived threat, tapping will not be effective until you address the fears and other strong emotions underlying your weight.

First, you find and address the reasons you are overweight. Only after easing the emotions around those reasons is there an open door to tapping for the positive.

We can, however, use positive tapping to help us become more specific. Tapping for what we want to be or to have can be used to identify the "yes, buts," or what Gary Craig called "Tail Enders," which may come up as we state affirmations or goals. For instance, behind the affirmation "I am slim and trim and at my ideal healthy weight" might be the Tail Ender, "Yes, but I have no willpower," or "It's too hard to be my ideal weight," or "Being fat runs in my family." Once you identify the underlying reason(s) holding you back from being at your ideal weight, you can begin to develop your Setup for tapping. Tapping on any Tail Enders you find will help you develop clarity about what you are really thinking and feeling so you can begin to use EFT to resolve those issues.

Until EFT loosens the hold of the negative Tail Enders (e.g., all my family is fat) and the negative emotions (e.g., I am disgusted with myself), none of the positive desires and goals can be reached. EFT balances the negative disruption around *what is*. The Setup prepares the energy system for the tapping and establishes acceptance of ourselves in spite of having the problem.

This is an essential component of the EFT Setup: to accept that you have a problem. Introducing a positive statement before dealing with the major parts of the negative issue is like ignoring the roots of the problem. This is much like pulling a weed out and leaving the roots; it just grows back. Using the EFT Setup on what you really feel while still accepting yourself anyway allows you to address and resolve the problem. For example, "Even though I am still angry that my sister made fun of me when I was six, and made me cry in front of my best friend Annie, and then slapped me for being a crybaby, I deeply and completely accept myself and how I feel," enables you to begin the process of neutralizing the emotional impact of the event.

Sometimes we are tempted to add in a statement of what we *think* we should feel instead of accepting what we *do* feel. Adding in wishful thinking before we accept ourselves for having the problem is more like saying, "I have this problem, and I wish I didn't." For example, you may want to say, "Even though I am still angry that my sister made fun of me when I was six, I appreciate her good points anyway." No, you don't! When you are very angry, it is impossible to appreciate the good points of the person who hurt you – even if you want to. *With EFT, we recognize the actual feeling first so we can accept that we have it before we can use EFT to let it go. The first step is to accept where we are and then work to where we want to be.*

Test Your Knowledge

1. Briefly explain in your own words why in EFT we focus on the problem (the "negative").

2. An essential component of the EFT Setup is to:

    a. solve your issues in as few sessions as possible.

    b. accept that you have a problem.

    c. convince yourself that you don't have a problem.

3. True or false? It is important in the EFT Setup to add in a statement of how you think you should feel.

4. What can you do if you are not comfortable with the acceptance statement?

5. True or false? Focusing on the positive is the best way to use EFT successfully.

Answers can be found in Appendix C

What to Do Before You Tap

There are three parts of the EFT process you need to identify prior to beginning tapping. They are: clarify the problem, create a specific setup, and decide how to test results.

Clarify the Problem

We've already said that clarifying your *specific* problem is the first step to a successful tapping experience. Our reactions to past events in life teach us how to react to similar situations in our future. We learned how to react to today's events at some point back in our past. Our goal is to identify when, where, and how we picked up the limiting belief or learned the problem behavior or developed sensitivity causing an overreaction. We then tap around that specific event. Many times, a problem will repeat itself. Try to work with the first time you can remember feeling that same way.

"I'm forty pounds overweight" may be your presenting problem. For EFT to be most effective, however, it is important to find the "reasons" for your presenting problem: those events that led to the development of limiting beliefs and core issues underneath the presenting problem. There are many possible underlying reasons for being overweight. What was going on in your life when you started to gain weight?

Perhaps you are subconsciously afraid of attaining your ideal weight. Perhaps losing weight might cause another person to be attracted to you, and you are afraid of threatening your marriage. Perhaps you overeat because you are unhappy with your family life or your job. Or you began overeating when you were passed over for a promotion or maybe when your favorite dog died. What event(s) led you to think or believe your "reason"? When you have found an underlying belief, now look for any event that created or is influencing that belief. Then you can tap for all the parts (aspects) of any associated past event(s) so you can begin to clear the negative conclusions around why you gained the weight. EFT works fastest when you find and clarify events underlying the presenting problem.

Physiological or Body Reaction: Finding a specific event or the underlying issue is often difficult, especially when working on your own problems. The alternative is to establish a mind-body connection. Note your body's reaction when you are tuned in to the problem you are addressing. Where exactly do you feel your reaction in your body? Describe it as best you can. *It is impossible to have an emotion without a corresponding physical reaction.* William James, one of the American founders of psychology, recognized this phenomenon as early as 1884. According to James, the body responds physically to any exciting event (whether positive or negative) and our perception of those physiological changes *is* emotion. An emotion actually arises from a physical sensation, so we can be sure that the body's physiological response is an integral part of the emotion we perceive. Becoming aware of this mind-body connection is very useful in using EFT to relieve emotional stress.

Create a Specific Setup

Create a Setup that addresses your specific event or physiological feeling as clearly as you can. If at the beginning you can't be totally specific, start with whatever feeling you are feeling *now*. Usually, as you tap, you remember related events or develop more clarity for the specific drivers behind your own reasons for your presenting problem. Even if you are starting on a more general or global statement, your goal is to get to a specific event. It is helpful to remember the little jingle (Adams 2006):

For results that are *terrific*, it helps to be *specific*.

This training resource will give you several tools to simplify the process of making the issue specific.

Adjusting the Setup: After developing your specific Setup and Reminder Phrase and then tapping the points, you will stop to measure the results. If your intensity is not resolved, don't be concerned. It is not unusual for an issue to take more than a few rounds of tapping. If this happens, modify your Setup and Reminder Phrase to reflect that you "*still* have some of this issue." There are two reasons for modifying the wording to reflect that you *still have some* of the issue. You want to keep the wording specific and recognize the current reality, which now is that *some* of the problem still exists. This practice also helps deal with any part of you (even subconsciously) that wants to hold on to the issue. Callahan felt that there was a distinct difference between getting over an issue and getting over an issue *completely*. The practice of adjusting the wording is to address any resistance to complete resolution of the issue.

Decide How to Test Results

The SUD scale of 0 to 10 is the most often used "test." Chapter 5 discusses using percentages, submodalities, and creative alternatives to test the intensity level of an issue. It doesn't matter which method you use to measure progress. The important point is to test your progress frequently. Generally, as you tap, the intensity level goes down. It could, however, stay the same or go up. Keep in mind, when checking your intensity level, there is no right or wrong answer; all answers are simply feedback. Usually, you will test your progress after every tapping round. If the intensity is high, however, you may wish to tap several rounds before you stop to test.

Let's look at how we addressed these three concepts – clarifying, developing a specific Setup, and testing – when we were doing the Constricted Breathing exercise:

1. Clarifying the problem. We established a mind-body connection. We assessed how well we were breathing at that moment in time. To do this, we had to notice how our body was breathing and noted how our body felt as we took our slow deep breaths.

2. Developing a specific Setup. We decided to work on how well we were breathing in the current moment.

3. Deciding how to test results. We decided to test the progress (or lack of progress) by using a percentage measure. We assessed what percentage of a full breath we were actually breathing at the time.

Test Your Knowledge

1. True or false? It is possible to have an emotion without a corresponding physical reaction.

2. What is SUD?

3. The cause of all negative emotions is:

   a. disruption in the body's energy system.

   b. a person's negative reaction to an event.

   c. the negative events in a person's life.

Answers can be found in Appendix C

Before Practicing on Yourself

As a beginner, you want to start with simple issues rather than complex ones. Generally, the more current issues (within the past three years) are less complex because there are usually fewer aspects with current issues, or they involve less complex components. Pick the current (and usually simpler) issues to start – those daily annoyances that affect us all: My boss yelled at me today; anger at the driver that cut in front of me on the way to work; my husband loads the dishwasher wrong; my son washed my favorite white blouse with his red shirt; I missed the bus; my friend embarrassed me telling that story in front of my date.

Hold off on the bigger ones until you are more comfortable with the process. Working with simple issues will normally give you quicker results. Complex issues can take time and may seem like you're not getting anywhere. Working with simple issues also helps you become familiar with EFT, gain confidence, become comfortable working with issues, and begin to understand the various aspects that issues can have.

Sometimes, however, what starts as a simple issue can lead to a deeper or more complex issue; simple issues may not stay simple. One student had the fear that she'd never learn the right words to say as an EFT practitioner – a typical concern for new learners. As she tapped on this issue, she realized that she often felt afraid of not being able to do things well. Tapping on a remembered event soon moved to her basic core issue: "I'm not good enough." This is a much more complex and time-consuming issue to address. Of course, EFT works with complex issues as well, but we want to begin with simple issues first. One has to learn to ride a bike before entering a bike race.

Exercise:
Remember a Scene

Think about a scene in a movie or TV program or a book you've read. Pick a scene that still affects you in some negative way.

- Pick a short scene, or part of a scene, that would be only a minute or less in length. Replay the scene in your head and note what you see, hear, feel, and think? Note, too, where you feel your reaction in your body.
- Give your overall reaction an intensity level of 0 to 10.
- Create a Setup: "Even though I have this [your reaction] to [your scene], I deeply and completely accept myself." Say the Setup three times as you tap the Karate Chop point. For example, "Even though I still shudder when I think about the ranger being spit on by the dinosaur, I deeply and completely accept myself."
- Create a Reminder Phrase. In this example, it could be "Spit on."
- Tap each of the Basic Recipe points: H (optional), EB, SE, UE, UN, Ch, CB, UA. Remember the head point can be omitted or tapped either at the beginning or at the end of each round.
- Measure your reaction.
- Repeat the Setup, modifying it to, "Even though I *still* have some reaction to this scene, I deeply and completely accept myself." Modify the Reminder Phrase to "This remaining feeling."

Notice as you tap if your attention switches to another part of the scene or jumps to an entirely different scene. If this happens, go with the new insight. In our example it could be "Even though I felt shock as I realized the ranger would die because of the spit, I deeply and completely accept myself." Repeat tapping until your number is 0. If you did shift to another part or scene, remember to go back to all the parts of any scene that came up and check to see if all the parts are down to 0.

Important: You may also find that your feelings about the scene change. First, your reaction was revolt at the spit, and then it could change to fear that the ranger will die. Your attention was, at first, on the scene just as the ranger turned. Then, as you tapped, you noticed more about the dinosaur. These various parts of the picture – what you saw, heard, felt, smelled, and tasted and the accompanying emotions – are called "aspects." This training resource will go into detail about handling these.

How to Get Specific

Getting specific is stressed throughout EFT workshops, training materials, and this training resource. But getting specific can be a challenge for beginners because people often begin with a general description of their problem. They may say, for example, I'm unhappy; people take advantage of me; I don't like my job; there is too much stress in my life; I can't sleep at night; I can't drive over that bridge; I'm in debt; I can't do anything right; I'm not cut out for relationships; my mother doesn't respect me; my husband doesn't pay any attention to me. All of these presenting problems are examples of global issues. With EFT, your goal is to get to a specific time and event in which you first felt that the global issue was a problem in your life – an event that, when you think about it, still gives rise to that same negative emotion.

In many circumstances, a specific issue starts off with the statement "The time when ..." Examples: *the time when* my father beat me; *the time when* my brother dragged me by the hair; *the time when* Johnny put a spider down my back; *the time when* we had the car wreck; *the time when* the engine on the plane caught fire; *the time* I missed the ball and made my team lose the game; *the time* my teacher called me stupid in class; *the time* the study group told me I was a poor writer; *the time when* the girl wouldn't kiss me on the swings; *the time when* my husband ignored me when I wanted to tell him about my success.

It can be helpful to ask questions to find the specific event that led to, or contributed to, the negative that you want to release.

Become an Investigative Reporter

Asking questions to get to a specific event is like being an investigative reporter. General descriptions of the problem are rarely the real problem. The real problem is some conclusion or belief you've formed about yourself or the world. *You need to find the events in your life that led to developing that belief.* Use the same questions reporters ask: Who? What? When? Where? How?

Questions are very powerful. Questions make us think about the issue in a more insightful way to help clarify the issue for tapping. Questions help us look at the problem from a new perspective. Questions help us get specific.

Here are some important questions to help find a specific issue:

- **How?** How do you know that? How does this happen? How did you learn that? How do you do that?
- **What?** What makes you think that? What has to happen for you to do/feel that? What other situations does this remind you of? What was happening the first time you felt that? What do you need to have before you can resolve this? What are you getting out of holding on to this? What keeps you from changing?
- **When?** When does that happen? When do you feel like that? When else in your life have you felt that way?

46

- **Who?** Who else in your life does that remind you of? Who was there when that happened?
- **Where?** Where were you when this happened? Where else does this affect you?

Why: to use it or not? When we are asked "Why?" we tend to get defensive. The question "Why did you do that?" seems to indicate we *should* have done something else. After all, if we knew clearly why we did something, we probably would have already addressed the issue. Often we don't have a good answer for "Why?" An EFT practitioner will focus on the questions who, what, when, where, how. Asking why often leads to a non answer, "I don't know." Asking why can have

someone defending his or her position and lead that person away from the real issue. You may find you hear a more receptive response to "How do know that is a problem?" versus "Why is that a problem?"

Your goal is to find specific events that led to developing the fear, belief, or conclusion you developed around the presenting problem. These fears, beliefs, and conclusions are what Gary Craig called the "Writing on Your Walls." The writing on your wall is composed of those "truths" you believe about yourself and the world; the suppositions you have made about yourself and the world; the learned information you consult every time you make a decision. Discovering these truths are helpful, but, to resolve them, you most often have to find and resolve what created the writing on your wall.

Let's give some sample questions for the problem description "My spouse does not respect me."

What happens to make you think that? *When* have you felt that same feeling before? *How* does she/he act (or *what* does she/he do) that makes you think that? *How* is that a problem for you? *When* do you feel most disrespected? Does your spouse remind you of anyone else in your life that you felt did not respect you? Are there other situations in which you do not feel respected? *What* happens then? *When* is the first time you remember not feeling respected by your spouse? *When* is the first time you can remember feeling disrespected? *How* are the events similar?

As you can see, most of the answers to these questions would start off with *the time when* … Important: If you don't get to a time when, keep asking questions until you do.

We all create meaning from everything that happens to us in our lives. We make some interpretation of every event. We make a conclusion about ourselves and/or the world. In the previous example, maybe you stay in a disrespectful relationship because you concluded from your childhood experiences by watching your parents that all men/women talk that way to women/men, and so you decided that is just "how it is."

In another example, remember *the time when* your mother yelled at you when your puppy tinkled in the house. You have dozens of choices as to how to interpret that event. You can conclude you are not a responsible person or, if she's yelled at you often, that you don't do anything right. You can conclude puppies get in the way of getting approval from important people in your life. You can decide dogs in general create problems for you. You can believe that women get upset easily and, to get love, you are responsible to keep them happy or that there's nothing you can do about it but suffer through.

As that child, we didn't have the adult perspective or reasoning skills to see that Mom was stressed with a job, three kids, not enough money, and no support system, and was expressing her frustration at what she saw as one more thing she'd have to do. As a child, we make everything all about us, and our subconscious carries that child perspective into adulthood. We are still making decisions based on what we decided about ourselves and the world at five or eight or ten or sixteen. Would we *now* go to a six-year-old for advice on how to live our lives? Even a sixteen-year-old? Of course not, but most of us are still operating from the decisions we made as a child or young adult.

Until you resolve *the time when* you created your "truth," you will continue to operate from that truth written on your wall.

Do You Always Get to a "Time When…"?

Not always. Sometimes we may not remember a time when. Try as we might, we can't recall anything specific. Perhaps it seems that "it has always been this way." You realize you must have experienced negative events but just can't seem to identify a specific one.

If this happens, you may need to tap generally about your issue before something specific comes up. It is not unusual for tapping to bring up memories we've forgotten. In the event you can't come up with a specific, this can be a good time to tap for the physiological response to your general problem description. This is a great way to tap when you can't find specifics. *Where do you feel your response to the problem in your body?* Tap for your physiological response. For example, "Even though I feel a burning lump in my stomach when I think about being rejected, I deeply and completely accept myself." Notice in this example that we gave a specific description of the physical feeling.

Truth Exercise

Think of one of your own absolute truths or a firmly held belief you have about yourself and/or the world. Use some of the questions listed previously to find where you developed that belief. Not all conclusions are negative, of course. Dark alleys in the city can be dangerous; it is not good to walk out in front of traffic.

What "truth" do you hold that limits your life in some way? Go back to the list of questions and see if you can come to one or more "time(s) when …" When you have a specific event, create a Setup from your *time when.* "Even though I have [this issue from the time when], I deeply and completely accept myself."

Examples of beliefs:

Don't rock the boat.	Money is evil.
It's not for people like us.	It can't be easy.
Don't expect much.	I'm too old.
Who do I think I am?	I'm not pretty enough.
Don't waste money.	To do it right, do it yourself.
I'm not smart enough.	Prepare for the worst.
Don't stand out in a crowd.	Know your place!
I'll never amount to anything.	Don't get your hopes up.
Why bother?	People only look out for themselves.
Walk softly and carry a big stick.	Money doesn't grow on trees.

Already Tuned In?

On the other hand, sometimes you find that you are already upset when thinking about an event. You are obviously already "tuned in" to a specific issue. In these cases, just start tapping for the immediate upset feeling. While your description of what is upsetting you might be a general statement, the emotions you are feeling are up front and center, and *are* specific. So, if you are already upset, just tap.

Important: Keep yourself safe! When on your own, don't work with issues that are overwhelming. If you suddenly become emotional, stop focusing on the emotional issue but *keep tapping,* until the emotion regulates. If necessary, seek assistance from a professional.

You can wait until after a few rounds of EFT, when there is some level of calm, to get more specific. As you tap to calm the immediate upset, you will begin to gain clarity on the "real" issue. There is much truth to the saying, "You are never upset by what you think you are upset about." There is often one, or more, earlier events that are contributing to the amount of upset you are feeling now.

Test Your Knowledge

1. True or false? Beginners should start with more complex issues rather than simpler ones.

2. Explain the importance of "getting specific."

3. What are the general detective questions you can ask to encourage specificity?

4. When tapping, if you become suddenly emotional, it is important to:

    a. stop tapping.

    b. take a break.

    c. keep tapping.

    d. take deep breaths until calmer.

Answers can be found in Appendix C

Aspects – The Pieces of Your Problem

Your presenting problem can be thought of as a puzzle with various pieces:

- The puzzle (your description of your presenting problem) has multiple pieces. You have to pick *one specific piece, or issue, at a time.*
- Each puzzle piece (issue) has several sides (aspects.) Most issues have *multiple aspects.* Often each side, or aspect, needs to be tapped on separately.
- Some pieces are more critical to completing the puzzle. These are often the *core issues* behind your presenting problem that must be addressed to solve the problem. Sometimes there are multiple causes and events that are linked to the problem.
- Other puzzle pieces seem to fall into place easily. When putting a puzzle together, sometimes it seems you search and search to find a particular piece. When you do find that elusive piece, it then seems that other pieces now easily fit into place. Dealing with our issues can be similar: we get one piece here and one piece there and finally we find our core issue; then

many of other related little pieces no longer seem so formidable. They were "put into place" when you found the core issue.

Most of our issues have multiple aspects and, at times, multiple related feelings or events. Fortunately, we don't have to tap for every single one of them! As we resolve some of the events, or when we find and resolve our core issue, many of our other related issues are resolved as well. In EFT, this phenomenon is called the "generalization effect," which often occurs after resolving several related events. Mary, Callahan's patient, identified her fear in her stomach. Focusing on her stomach feeling allowed just one point, under the eye, to resolve her entire phobia of water. When she resolved the fear in her stomach, the other "pieces" fell into place.

The "easy" issues, like the easy pieces in putting a puzzle together, can be resolved so quickly they are called a "one-minute wonder." Puzzles with large numbers of pieces and complex pictures can take much longer to complete. Don't get discouraged when working on your presenting problem if some, or even all, the pieces seem difficult to find and fit into completing the picture. Perseverance and detective work is important in these situations. At times, it is helpful to have another EFTer to aid you in finding your own critical pieces.

Daisy Chains

EFT can work so rapidly and efficiently that you may shift to another aspect of the same issue, or jump to another related issue. This can happen in a daisy-chain fashion from issue, to issue, to issue. The daisy-chain effect is an opportunity to address multiple issues effectively in one session. Therefore, as Gary Craig says, "When on a roll, keep rolling!" A good example of the daisy-chain effect can be found on Gary Craig's DVD, *The EFT Course,* Part II, #4, where he works with Marlys.

Sometimes when you switch to another aspect or another event, it is obvious. You start tapping for the tension in your shoulders and, suddenly, the anger at your boss pops into your mind and is a much stronger feeling than the tension in your shoulders. Other times, you may not notice that you switch aspects or events at all. You may begin working on one situation about your sister and, as you tap, your thoughts shift to another situation with your sister and then to another. It's all about your sister, so you are not consciously realizing that your frustration has shifted to sadness, anger, resentment, or another feeling.

Your subconscious links what it considers related events or reactions and often brings these up as you tap. Because of this you may cover a variety of issues, and aspects of those issues, in your tapping. This can be both beneficial and counterproductive. You may jump to a different "daisy" before you've dealt with all the petals from the first one. Being aware of this daisy-chain possibility will help you identify when you shift to another issue, event, or emotion. It's often helpful to write down your issue and your intensity. If you begin with "My anger is a 10," and you then start feeling sad as you tap, write down, "Sadness is a 9." After tapping for the sadness, make sure you go back and check the intensity of the anger you had originally. There could be many emotions and aspects, which is why it is helpful to write down what you are tapping on and your response.

This chaining effect may lead you to a different scene in the same event or to a different emotion or aspect of the same event. You may also jump to a different event related to the same overall issue. These are all good things. Simply make a note of them so you can go back and make sure each has been resolved. A common mistake beginners make is to stop tapping for any issue when they feel "better." If you had an intensity of an 8 on your anger at the teacher, and you tapped it down to a 3, you will feel "better." *Don't stop there.* Continue following your own daisy chain until your anger is 0. Many students of EFT are walking around feeling better (lower intensity) about their situation but not free from its impact. Don't settle for "better"; go for complete freedom – keep tapping until your aspect or issue is 0.

Examples of Changing Aspects

Different scene	Same event
Different event	Same reaction or emotion
Different emotion	Same event
Different event	Related to your reaction

For example, you start tapping for an automobile accident you had five years ago. You start with *the time when* you first realized the other car would hit you, and you are overcome with fear because you were helpless to prevent the car hitting you. Your intensity when you think about it is an 8. You tap, "Even though I feel helpless with the car coming at me, I deeply and completely accept myself." As you are tapping the points with your Reminder Phrase, "Helplessness," you shift to *the time when* the car was folding up in front of you and then to the look on the other people's faces. Since the common denominator is the car accident and the feeling of helplessness, the shift to the other scenes may not even be noticeable to you. These are, however, different aspects of the same event. Noticing shifts to another aspect or to another related event is important. To use EFT successfully, you need to go back to check that each aspect has been fully addressed. If you miss testing an aspect, you may miss having the event resolved.

It is OK to keep tapping on each new aspect, emotion, scene, event, and issue as they appear, but remember, before you end your tapping session, go back to the beginning of *the time when* your event started and check to see that *each* part was reduced to 0. If any part of it is not completely cleared, keep the event on your tapping list for your next tapping time.

Gary Craig gives an example of the daisy-chain effect on one of his early audiotapes. He was working over the phone with a man who had a fear of heights. Since the man was a roofer, he was confronted with his fear every time he went to work. Gary asked the man to make a movie of one of the worst times when he was afraid (see the Movie Technique in the next chapter). They tapped the incident and all aspects. The roofer reported going from a 10 to a 0. Gary then attempted to test the results by asking the man to rerun his movie. The man reported his fear was an 8; they tapped it to 0. When tested by rerunning the movie again, surprisingly, the man reported a 9. The next test after a round of tapping revealed another high number. Generally, the test numbers after tapping do not keep going back up. In this instance, the man was going on to the next situation in which he experienced a fear of heights. After each round of EFT that brought his fear in one situation to 0, he was switching to a *different* roofing experience.

When you are working with others, they may tell you about the next issue that comes up and the daisy-chain process is obvious. Alternately, remember it is not always clear when aspects of an issue change – even to yourself! Asking after each tapping round, "What comes up now?" can help you identify when an aspect changes.

Possible Aspects for "Fear of Flying"

Feeling Trapped · FEAR OF CRASHING · PANIC · Takeoff and/or Landing · FEAR OF DEATH · No Control · Fear of Crowds · Fear of Loud Sounds · Wasting Money · Birds Might Fly into the Engine · Rumbling, Shaking of Plane · No Escape

(Davidson 2009)

Fear Exercise

Think of a phobia or fear you or someone you know may have. Then list all the aspects you can think of around it. This is very good practice and will make it easier for you to explore your aspects for any issue when working with EFT.

Note: When doing this exercise with others, never assume that the aspects someone else has around an issue are the same as you have.

Peeling Onions

Gary Craig used this metaphor to describe the process of working through layers of issues. The more complicated an issue, the more layers, aspects, or issues it may have.

Working with each layer, or "peeling off" these layers one by one is important for complete resolution. Each aspect has a different feeling to it even if the difference is slight. Suppose you were passed over for a promotion. You may start out feeling angry that your boss didn't appreciate your work or that a coworker sabotaged your chance for promotion.

You may move to the guilt that you felt when you told your spouse you didn't get the promotion, moving then to your spouse's reaction to the news, then to shame that your friends would think you weren't good enough. Each of these feelings, or aspects, need to be addressed separately with EFT. It can be in the same "session" but addressed singularly. You continue working with each layer as it comes up. The goal is to keep tapping on each aspect until all of them are resolved.

Sometimes, particularly when working with long-standing beliefs or heavily traumatic experiences, you may work through the events and aspects with EFT only to find later that lingering pieces of the belief or trauma come up. These are new aspects of the issue that were not addressed or not addressed completely with EFT when you worked on it. Be persistent. It may take a good while to reach complete resolution.

We become attached to and comfortable with "our own stuff." Often, we have to deal with the *resistance* we have to getting over the issue before we are able to *resolve* it. We're torn about letting go of our stuff, sometimes without even realizing it; parts of us want to, and parts of us don't. We may have to deal with identity issues that could be attached. For whatever reason, you may feel, "This is who I am, and it is not possible to change, or "This is who I am, and I don't want to change." Even when we truly believe that we *want* to change, there is often a subconscious or inner fear of "What will happen if I change," or "Who would I then be?" Tap for the part of yourself that doesn't want to get over it, no matter how small that part may be. That part has a good reason, even if it seems to be an irrational reason, for wanting to keep the issue. Tap to resolve the I-want-to-I-don't-want-to conflict, "Even though part of me wants to resolve this and part of me seems *not* to want to resolve this, I deeply and completely accept *all* parts of me." Another common Setup would be, "Even though I have a conflict about resolving this, I deeply and completely accept where I am and how I feel about it."

You could feel guilty for feeling or doing something you may think is "wrong." We have so many ways we can "punish" ourselves. "Even though I feel guilty about this because I think it is wrong, I deeply and completely accept how I feel."

Or you could feel guilty that you are resistant to change. In that case, tap for the guilt around any issue as another aspect(s). It's important to be kind to yourself here; after all, it is very human to *not* want to change. All changes are a bit scary, even the changes that you truly believe you want. There is no magic crystal ball that will answer, "What *will* happen if I change something?" A possible Setup could be, "Even though I really don't want to change this and I don't know what will happen if I change this, I deeply and completely accept myself and my feelings."

When working with EFT as self-help, it is often beneficial to tap several rounds on "this resistance" to whatever issue you'd like resolved. When possible, be as specific as you can when tapping for your resistance. Most of our long-standing issues are wrapped into our definition of "self," and, therefore, resistance to change is a typical reaction. We may only be vaguely aware we have resistance to resolving our issue. We may not realize we have any resistance at all. Other times, we are very clear that we are getting something positive from having the issue and are therefore resisting.

It is helpful to ask questions about what the upside is and what is the downside? "What am I getting out of holding on to this?" Or "What would I be losing if I let this go?" Or "If I weren't dealing with this, what would I have to be doing?"

For example, there was a woman who had a bad back. Her children would come to her home and help her do chores, go to the grocery store, and more. She truly believed she wanted her back to stop hurting. However, when asked the question "Would anything negative happen if your back was healed?" she realized that she was afraid her children would stop coming to see her and helping her. This belief was creating resistance to releasing her back pain. This aspect had to be addressed before tapping for her back problem could be effective. Finding such core issues of resistance can sometimes be a challenge; we are not always aware of our resistance, so it may take some detective work to find it. You will learn more about dealing with limiting beliefs in level 2.

Test Your Knowledge

1. Most issues have:

   a. one aspect.

   b. a couple aspects.

   c. many aspects.

   d. no aspects.

2. Explain the concept of "daisy chains."

3. True or false? The more layers an issue has, the more complicated it is to resolve it.

Answers can be found in Appendix C

Issues with Fewer Aspects

Sometimes simple issues with just a few aspects can be resolved in a very short period of time with EFT, usually within an hour, or even within a few rounds. Just as a jigsaw puzzle with fewer pieces is generally put together more quickly than one with many more pieces, occasionally, issues are resolved very quickly using EFT. Phobias, for instance, are often, but not always, easily collapsed with only a few rounds of tapping. As noted earlier, such quick resolution is called a "one-minute wonder." There are many articles giving examples of one-minute wonders. It's extremely gratifying to see a long-standing fear or issue collapse quickly with just a few rounds of EFT. However, *these situations are the exception and not the rule.* Although it's wonderful when lasting change occurs so quickly, most issues have multiple aspects and several related events that must be resolved before completely collapsing the issue. Don't give up. Keep tapping. Persistence and detective work will pay off in the end.

Real Life

Thinking about a situation causes the same energy disruption as being in the actual situation would. Remember it is the *thought that causes the energy disruption,* rather than the event itself. A common question when first learning EFT is some variation on "I tapped away my fear of spiders while thinking about them, but what if I actually see a spider in the room?" Although you can cover many aspects just by imagining the issue, being in the real situation can bring up new aspects not considered or remembered during a tapping session. It's possible that you didn't get to all the aspects or core issues. Therefore, if any new aspects should come up in the real-life situation, you can tap on those now identified aspects.

Let's say you've tapped for your fear of snakes. You've tapped for any situation in which you encountered a snake or situations in which someone frightened you with a story about a snake. You've tapped for imagining a snake; you've tapped while looking at a picture of a snake; you've tapped for one snake, lots of snakes, curled up snakes, moving snakes, and every position you can think a snake could be in. You feel ready to test the results of your tapping by going to a pet store. When you get to the store and actually see a snake, you realize you didn't tap for the aspect of seeing a snake with its tongue flicking in and out. So you now tap for the moving tongue and realize you still have some fear of being close to a snake. You move farther back and tap until you are able to move closer. You might also realize that you are actually afraid of snakes because someone's tongue reminded you of a snake! Simply follow the path and keep tapping.

Important to remember: Tapping away fears and phobias does not take away self-preservation. *The goal of tapping away your over-the-top emotional reaction(s) is to give you a choice.* You are not, all of a sudden, going to decide to become a poisonous snake handler. Also, do not push yourself to "get over" a fear. Continue to tap and only take each next step as you feel comfortable.

Aspect Exercise

Some problems have only a few aspects. Some have many, many aspects. Go back to the list of aspects you made in the Fear Exercise. Use EFT separately for each aspect. Watch for any new aspects that may appear as you are working down your list. It is possible to daisy chain to other related problems; for example, the real problem behind fear of spiders turns out to be the abuse you experienced from your sister as a young child.

When something new comes up, write down the newly remembered event or emotion, then go on to finish tapping with the current aspect and event you started with until 0 or you have no further movement on it. You can then refer back to your list and continue using EFT to work on the next aspect or issue.

Sound complicated? Resolving a phobia *can* be very simple. But it can also possibly become complex. Don't get overwhelmed. Handle aspects one at a time. It generally has taken a long time to get where you are now, so be patient as you work to resolve the issue. Create a list of all the aspects you can think of around your issue, then pick one and get started. Remember that, although it may be possible to have an issue, fear, or event with only one aspect, it is rare; so don't give up. Be persistent.

As you tap down your list of aspects, you may notice you become calmer and less emotional; at other times, you may not experience any relief until you have dealt with all the related aspects. Both experiences are normal.

You can also seek assistance from a more experienced EFT practitioner. We all need help sometimes, no matter how experienced we are.

Test Your Knowledge

1. *In your own words, describe "aspects."*

2. *The point of tapping for a phobia is to give you:*

   a. the desire to be confronted with the object of your fear.

   b. a choice.

   c. no choice.

3. *True or false? New aspects can appear while tapping.*

Answers can be found in Appendix C

Physical Responses Associated with Emotion

You are beginning to see that, to be successful using EFT, it is important to be persistent and to keep tapping on each aspect and related issue that comes to your attention.

Let's look at another way to approach your problem. Remember that the physiological response *is* the emotion. Sometimes, when it's difficult to articulate an emotion, or to find a specific event, it is possible to work with the physiological response associated with the emotion. EFT works just as well when you work with your body's response.

- *Where* is the feeling in your body?
- *How* would you describe it?

When you can identify and describe the physical feelings around your issue, you can use your definition as your specific issue. Develop a Setup and Reminder Phrase for whatever physical feeling you identified: this sick yucky feeling in my stomach, this choking sensation in my throat, this elephant sitting on my body, this suffocating feeling in my chest, or this ball in my stomach. Do not worry if your description is *real* or not. There is no real "ball" in your stomach. You don't have to worry about what your description means. As the ball in your stomach dissolves as you tap, your emotion decreases as well.

Check the intensity of the physical feeling by assigning it a number between 0 and 10. A possible Setup could be "Even though I have this ball in my stomach, I deeply and completely accept myself." Continue by tapping all the EFT points using the Reminder Phrase, "This ball in my stomach." After each round of EFT, notice if the feeling moves or changes. Continue tapping using the new place or feeling until the intensity tests at 0. Be persistent; it may take many rounds.

Note: Some people have developed the coping skill that dissociates them from emotion and the physical impact of an emotion. This keeps them unaware of or denying any emotion or physical affect. EFT can still be used in these cases, but doing so is beyond the scope of this level 1 training resource.

Physical Feeling Exercise

Now let's try this. Pick a small issue in your own life. (Small means that, when you think about it, the intensity is a 5 or below.)
- Where is the feeling in your body?
- How would you describe it?
- What intensity number would you give the physical feeling?
- Tap the Karate Chop point (or rub the Sore Spot) as you say three times, "Even though I have [your description of the physical feeling in your body], I deeply and completely accept myself anyway."
- Tap each EFT point as you say your Reminder Phrase [brief description of the feeling in your body].
- Continue tapping the points until your intensity number goes to 0, or until your description of the physiological response changes.
- If your description changes, change the Setup and Reminder Phrase to fit the new description. Follow any movement of your physical response or any change in the description. Continue tapping until there is no longer a response and the number is 0. Then go back to the "small issue" you started with. Is the intensity on it the same? Has it changed? What comes up for you now that you are revisiting this issue? If the intensity is a 0, you have resolved that issue. If the issue has now brought up other underlying issues or "daisy chained" to a different aspect, create another appropriate Setup and continue tapping.

The Generalization Effect

In Gary Craig's *The EFT Manual* (2008), the metaphor of the forest and the trees is used to describe the generalization effect.

You have a problematic issue (forest) with many events (trees), often with many aspects (branches), making up that forest. To resolve the issue, you have to address relevant events and aspects. To remove a real forest, you cut down one tree at a time.

To resolve an issue with EFT, no matter how large the issue, you address one event or feeling (tree) at the time.

EFT is designed to address one specific event or memory at a time. To fully resolve your issue, identifying and tapping for multiple aspects around that memory *may be necessary*. Fortunately, due to the generalization effect, it is *not always necessary* to tap for every aspect

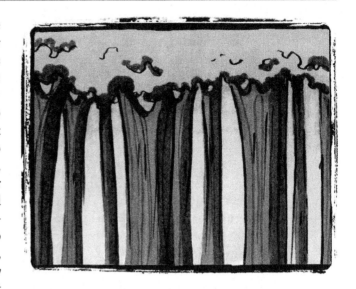

around an event or every memory that created a problematic limiting belief. Sometimes, as the energy is balanced around a few of the related aspects or memories, the entire issue is balanced as well.

An example of the generalization effect can be found on Gary Craig's EFT DVD, *The EFT Course: Six Days at the VA*. Gary Craig worked with Rich, a Vietnam veteran who suffered from PTSD for many years and was under treatment through the Veteran's Administration. Rich had experienced many horrific traumatic events during his military experience, but, as he worked with Craig and resolved some of the traumatic memories, his emotional response to many other memories collapsed as well.

Karin Davidson describes the effect as a beaver dam. Imagine the logs are events that contributed to your issue. You don't have to clear or remove *all* the logs to make the dam weak enough to collapse. Keep tapping around each "log" and soon all the logs, the entire issue, will be washed away. The earlier or lower logs in the dam represent your childhood events and the upper logs the more recent events. Many practitioners believe that, for complex issues, it's better to try to locate the *first* time you had the feeling about your issue and work on that event. Dealing with childhood issues first is like removing the lower logs first, which could break the issue dam sooner, without having to tap on *all* the events regarding the same issue. For example, if your issue is that you have a problem asserting yourself because your father always said negative things about you, start with the first time you can remember him saying something negative to you. Often, as you start by tapping on an early memory, an even earlier memory comes up. Start with what you do remember. You can't always get to the lower logs until you have removed some of the top ones.

The generalization effect means you don't necessarily have to tap for every aspect of a memory to collapse it. If you have addressed and tapped for a few of the main events and feelings (the key events and feelings holding that logjam in place), the entire issue can collapse. As your energy system is balanced around a few of the key aspects or attributes of your issue, the connected parts are balanced as well.

The benefits from balancing or neutralizing the foundational events or aspects can generalize to other similar experiences as well. Relieving your phobia of spiders could resolve your negative emotions around your sister's treatment of you as a child, which may or may not include her scaring you with a spider.

You can see the generalization effect at work, too, when you tap for an emotional experience and you notice the pain in your shoulder is gone. Or you tap for the specific pain in your knee and find that your lower back pain is relieved. Or you may notice as you relieve the pain in your neck that the behavior of your coworkers no longer triggers an angry reaction.

Do You Always Tap for a Specific Aspect or Event?

The short answer is yes ... and no. As we have seen earlier, while we work diligently to get to a specific aspect or event, there are times when it is either not possible or not practical (or maybe not even safe; for example, it may cause a significant emotional upset). In EFT, it is *not* usually helpful to tap for an overly general belief: I am useless; I have a poor self-image; I am unlovable; I can't do anything right; I am not good enough. Maybe, if you tapped for such a general problematic statement every day for a *very* long time, your subconscious might identify enough issues and aspects for you to resolve it – maybe. As Gary Craig says, tapping for a general statement of your problem is like cutting off just the tips of the bad trees. Those negative trees are all still standing there.

Note: Craig believes that one of the most serious mistakes that EFT learners can make is attempting to use EFT on issues that are too large, complex, or global. New EFTers may be able to make progress on a global issue if they are persistent, but, if this takes a long time, they may give up too quickly. When they are able to break the problem down into specific events, they will see faster results and be encouraged to continue.

When you can't seem to identify any events behind your issue, try tapping on your physical response every time you have a related negative thought. Notice what comes up as you tap; follow the new thought or feeling as you tap.

There are times when you are already upset by an event and obviously already tuned in. This is the time to "just tap." You can tap using a general statement such as "This upset," or you can say nothing at all, just tap. The intention of EFT is to be as gentle as possible. *When the emotions are already strong, you don't want to increase the emotion.* Simply tap and keep tapping until you are calmer. Gary Craig calls this "taking the edge off" excessive emotion, and it is one of the few times when you tap for generalities rather than specifics. While "this upset" is a general statement, the emotions you are addressing are up front and your physiological responses are specific at that point. You will, consciously and subconsciously, tune to what is important for you right at that moment. In this case, just tap; don't worry about Setups or words or trying to develop anything specific.

Test Your Knowledge

1. True or false? It is important to describe your physical response to an emotion as accurately as possible.

2. The metaphor of the "forest" and the "trees" explains:

   a. daisy chains.

   b. the generalization effect.

   c. the apex effect.

   d. peeling the onion.

3. According to Gary Craig, what is the biggest mistake that new EFT students can make?

Answers can be found in Appendix C

EFT Methods

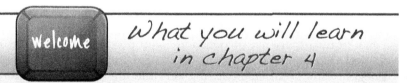

What you will learn in chapter 4

What creates trauma

Don't go where you don't belong

The Tearless Trauma Technique

The Movie Technique

The Tell the Story Technique

How to work with clients

Deal with things that come up

About Trauma

There are big "T" traumas and little "t" traumatic events. Although level 1 does not give you the in-depth skills to deal with big "T" or serious emotional responses to trauma, we discuss here some of what creates trauma and the symptoms of someone who is traumatized.

A trauma is something that happens that is *Unexpected, Dramatic, Isolating*, and you have *No strategy* to deal with it (UDIN).

Unexpected, sudden, shocking; a violation of expectations – *I never expected it.*

Dramatic; overwhelming; a threat to survival or identity – *It's too much.*

Isolating – *I'm on my own.*

No strategy, causing feelings of powerlessness; swamping your coping abilities – *There's nothing I can do.*

EFT practitioner David MacKay offers a different acronym – UTAP:

Unexpected

Threatening

Alone

Powerless

Trauma isn't always those obvious large events. The event can simply seem large to the person who experienced it. A little "t" trauma could be as simple as a look from Daddy, which was perceived by a five-year-old as threatening because it was unexpected, dramatic, and isolating, and the child had no strategy with which to address it, leaving the child feeling powerless and helpless.

Trauma specialist Dr. Robert Scaer writes:

> [A]ny negative life event occurring in a state of relative helplessness – a car accident, the sudden death of a loved one, a frightening medical procedure, a significant experience of rejection – can produce the same neurophysiological changes in the brain as do combat, rape, or abuse. What makes a negative life event traumatizing isn't the life-threatening nature of the event, but rather the degree of helplessness it engenders and one's history of prior trauma. (Scaer 2006, 50)

When something traumatic (UDIN) happens, it can lead to, among other effects:

- Disturbances in energy meridians
- Fight, flight, or freeze reactions
- Physical and emotional symptoms
- Your system becoming sensitized to similar events so that it recreates the traumatic symptoms
- Your experiences leading you to create distorted beliefs about yourself and the world

Symptoms of traumatic stress include flashbacks, hypersensitivity to triggers, panic and anxiety disorders, insomnia and nightmares, dissociation, depression and despair, inability to cope in some situations, physical symptoms, and more.

How do you know it's a trauma? As one client said, "It sticks in your head." After a trauma someone may then:

- Relive the trauma as a current event with no sense of time passed
- Have the sensory experience of the *then* and *there* time of the trauma
- Experience all the emotional and physical response of the event
- Have a fixation on the past
- Be unable to distinguish *then* from *now*
- Be unable to give a realistic meaning to the emotions, behaviors, and body sensations one is experiencing
- Be obsessed with avoiding triggers
- Be constantly vigilant for danger
- Be inarticulate and nonverbal about the experiences – "There are no words for this."

ve the event. As another client stated,
t back there like it was still happening."
ergency responses to the original threat
pent keeping emotions under control at
eality of here and now.

You Don't Belong

your scope of practice and in accordance
al guidelines. We are introducing trauma
small issue and ask questions to find a
EFT often deals beautifully with serious
atic stress disorder). Even if you are a
ld only provide services within the scope
T training does not prepare you to deal
unlicensed, unless you have the training
people who have long-term trauma, do
ma experience – even your own. Develop
nce.

referral sources and ...

Various EFT Methods

There are several EFT methods that were developed to address various issues, as gently and painlessly as possible. In level 1, you will learn three important EFT workhorses: the Tearless Trauma Technique, the Movie Technique, and the Tell the Story Technique. Level 2 will teach you additional EFT practices to expand your skills.

Tearless Trauma Technique – Guessing the Intensity

In some circumstances, the event may seem too upsetting even to *begin* to think about it. With the Tearless Trauma Technique, you identify a specific incident but do *not* tune in directly to the incident. You only need to *guess* at the emotional intensity.

Note: the name Tearless Trauma is a bit of a misnomer as it is not necessary to have a "trauma," big or little, to use this technique – just a realization that if you were to address a particular event, you would have an uncomfortable level of upset. The technique was designed to make addressing one's issues as gentle as possible.

The Tearless Trauma Technique is a form of imaginary scaling. Rather than becoming more upset by tuning in directly to the event, you simply guess at the intensity you *might* have *if* you did tune in to the disturbing event. You will have a sense of what the intensity would be. The accuracy of the number is not important. You are just looking for a baseline against which to measure progress. EFT is meant to be as gentle as possible. Remember *the goal is to relieve the upset – not relive it*. Guessing the intensity is a good method to use, especially in situations in which even slightly tuning in to your issue could create high intensity.

With the Tearless Trauma Technique, you don't try to picture *the time when*. You begin tapping using a generic Reminder Phrase: this problem, this upset, this fear. Continue tapping, stopping every few rounds to recheck your guess as to the intensity *if* you were to focus on it.

Only after you guess that the intensity would be very low do you attempt to imagine the incident. *Ideally, the guess of "intensity" should be 3 or below before you go into the incident at all.* If the intensity rises at any point as you imagine the situation, stop and tap on any remaining emotion, aspect, or physical reaction.

Some EFT practitioners help their clients keep the memory at bay by telling them to put the incident behind a thick curtain or wall, across the street, or in a closed box. The goal of Tearless Trauma is to dissociate yourself (or your client) from the event so that it is less upsetting.

The Movie Technique

The Movie Technique is one of the most basic EFT methods and has been used successfully for self-help and by EFT practitioners for over eighteen years. As described in Craig's original EFT manual, a movie begins at a specific place and time. It has specific characters, a specific plot, and specific words and actions; generates specific feelings; and ends at a specific point in time. When you make a movie of your issue, you are focusing on specifics. If you can't make a movie of your issue, then your issue is too global for EFT to work effectively. In fact, it is helpful to focus on just one scene at a time from your movie.

Did you see the movie *Titanic*? If so, as you think about the movie, you immediately see an image or hear a bit of the soundtrack. You are tuned in to a specific part of the movie *Titanic*. This works just as well with your own "movie." You don't have to run your entire movie to be tuned in to a significant part.

You can use the Movie Technique when working alone. Remember to tap for any intensity as you run the movie of your event. The Movie Technique is a dissociative technique to help decrease emotional intensity. (In the Tearless Trauma Technique, with the guessing, you, in effect, double dissociate from the event.)

Steps for the Movie Technique

1. Identify a specific event relating to your issue. Focus on one scene in your "movie." Make sure your movie scene is less than three minutes. Pay attention to as many details as possible. Clarify the details – what you see, hear, feel, smell, and taste. Remember any thoughts you had at the time.

    Note: If you begin to feel upset when just thinking of going into the details about your movie, tap in a general way for "Even though thinking about dealing with this movie upsets me, I deeply and completely accept myself anyway." Remember that, when you have intensity, you are tuned in to some emotion. Start tapping. When the intensity is down, go back to the issue and begin looking for related aspects. Be persistent and go for complete resolution. If the intensity is high, start by *not* focusing on the event. Start tapping for your emotions about looking at the event.

2.   Give the movie a representative title.
3.   Run the movie in your mind and evaluate its intensity level.
4.   Use the Setup. "Even though I have this [title] movie, I deeply and completely accept myself."
5.   Do several rounds of EFT, using the title of the movie as your Reminder Phrase.
6.   Evaluate the intensity now. If there is any intensity, keep tapping until it is 0.
     Note: Before moving to the next step, continue tapping, using the title of the movie, until the intensity is 0.
7.   Narrate the movie; *stop* at *any* point in the movie where there is intensity. Tap until that aspect is 0.
8.   Continue the story that makes up the movie. Work on any intensity until you can tell the entire story with no intensity.
9.   You can now move on to the next related event for your issue.

When using EFT on your own, it can be helpful to stand in front of a mirror and tell yourself the story to bring up any hidden aspects. Tap for *any* level of upset.

Some EFTers, especially when working on their own, are tempted to stop at a low intensity believing that "this is as good as it gets." Continue looking for aspects and related events until your issue is a 0. This may take several rounds or several tapping sessions. Be persistent. When working alone, it is sometimes difficult to address issues causing high intensity. It is very human to not go where we know there is pain. Remember to keep yourself safe. In cases of high intensity, an experienced practitioner can help.

Techniques for Practitioners

(*Note:* Please see the section on ethics in chapter 8. Always practice only within the scope of your training and license.)

The presenting problem a client brings to a session is usually not specific. Your role is to help your client identify specific events. You want the client to identify events underneath their presenting problem. What has happened in their life that contributes to keeping their presenting problem a problem? If they come in with anxiety or other upset, you start by focusing on and tapping for the current level of emotion. But your goal is to find a specific event behind their presenting problem. Sometimes, as they begin to tell you their story, they become upset. For some, just beginning to think about an event brings up a high intensity. If the intensity is high, *stop* them from continuing to talk; just tap. They *are* tuned in – being tuned in *is* specific. Tap several rounds on a generic "Even though I have this [emotion], I deeply and completely accept myself." Reminder phrase, "This [emotion]." When the client is calmer, go back to the story or ask more questions to find a specific event.

EFT has two very helpful techniques for getting specific: the Tell the Story Technique and the Movie Technique.

The Tell the Story Technique for Practitioners

The most used EFT method is to have your client simply tell the story of what happened and then tap, *using their own words*, for any upset that arises. The Tell the Story Technique is simply telling the story of what happened – the time when. You may wish to tap for the upset about telling the story before the client actually starts telling the story. You then *stop and tap at any point of emotional intensity*. Gary Craig's instructions for the Tell the Story Technique follow.

Each point of emotional intensity represents another aspect of the story. As a practitioner, your job is to help identify then tap for the key words around the particular upsetting aspect. Tapping can bring up other important aspects that can lead to even deeper issues. Let the client lead where the aspect goes – always use the client's words. But you may ask questions for clarification along the way. Work to clear each aspect as it comes up before going to the next one. If the client brings up another aspect before the first one is finished, write down the new aspect, but complete tapping on the first one. The only exception to this would be if the client's intensity does not lower. Then it may be necessary to go to the other aspect to clear it. *Always, always go back to make sure the other aspect's intensity is down.*

Remember, stop and tap at *any* sign of intensity, no matter how small. After telling the entire story, go back and check on all the aspects and continue tapping until all aspects are resolved and the entire story can be repeated without any upset.

In Gary Craig's tutorial #12, "The Tell the Story Technique: An Important Tool for Being Thorough," he gave the following guidelines for using this helpful method:

1. After describing the "Tell the Story Technique" to the client, ask them how they feel now about the mere thought of telling the story. Often you will get some substantial intensity at this stage and, if so, it is worthwhile to do a few global type rounds of EFT to take the edge off.

    "Even though I'm nervous about telling the story ..."
    "Even though I'm afraid what might happen when I tell this story ..."
    "Even though I don't like this whole thing ..."
    "Even though just starting the story gives me the jitters ..."

2. When the client feels comfortable about starting the story (perhaps an intensity level of 0–2), ask them to begin at a time when there is nothing to be concerned about. An example might be having lunch with a friend just before having a car accident. This tends to ease the client into the experience.

3. Instruct the client to stop the moment they feel any intensity whatsoever. This is critical to the success of this procedure. Most clients are conditioned by conventional techniques to "be courageous" and to "feel the feelings" and to "be brave and gut through it." Thus they are likely to go right by an important tapping point without telling you. The client needs to understand that if they don't stop, they have missed a healing opportunity. Hit this one hard. Emphasize it. Raise your voice a bit to punctuate it. Insist on it. Remind them that we are looking for minimal pain here and that they get no points for bravery.

4. Have the client repeat the story while doing EFT until they can tell it nonchalantly – like it was a shopping trip.

5. Then ask the client to close their eyes and vividly imagine the whole event. Ask them to try to get themselves upset by exaggerating the sights, sounds, and feelings. Chances are they will get through it fine; but, if they don't, you will have uncovered an important aspect or underlying cause. Use EFT for whatever comes up until they cannot get upset about the issue by either imagining it or talking about it.

6. The ultimate test, of course, will be physically to visit the scene or person again and see if anything else arises. If there are any remnants left, they will show up during the "real deal."

There are several benefits of using the Tell the Story Technique. Since clients expect to talk about their problems, this method seems more "normal." Related aspects are uncovered as their stories unfold. You can easily see how the session is progressing as you listen. Have the client tap for each upsetting aspect (tap with them as well.) Note: *It is also helpful while listening to the story to repeat just a few of the client's words back at pauses in the story.* You can use the Tell the Story Technique by itself or as a way to test results after using another EFT method.

Some practitioners have the client tap the entire time they are telling the story. Some have the client pick one favorite tapping point and just tap on that one while telling the story. Although this can be useful, keep in mind that this would be generic tapping to help decrease overall intensity. Be sure to stop at any sign of emotional upset and focus on that aspect.

Self-Help – There are many versions of the Tell the Story Technique for those who would like to use EFT for themselves. Although not developed in original EFT, many EFTers use terms such as: Tap and Talk, Tap and Vent, Tap and Rant. Simply tapping on the points while you describe your feelings and the event calms you.

EFT Master Lindsay Kenny, (2009) writes

Giving a *voice* to your feelings in this way helps collect different aspects of the problem ... This "stream of consciousness ranting" is very powerful and effective.

Just let the words come out as you tap ... If additional intensity comes up while tapping, do another round or two using the same method and words, or add more phrases and feelings. It's incredibly liberating to vent while tapping and often alleviates several aspects of the issue. Don't be surprised if the word hate comes up (among other things). Allow yourself the freedom to express how you felt at the time.

The Movie Technique for Practitioners

Let's go back over the instructions for the Movie Technique as if you were an EFT facilitator. Work first to decrease the client's current anxiety about looking at their issue at all. Tap to decrease any high emotional levels the client may have when they are just thinking about addressing the event.

Ask the client if they can make a short movie of the event. If so, ask how long the movie would be. The movie needs to be short; no longer than three minutes, preferably less. Often, events that upset us the most happen in only seconds. You will tap for each intense scene separately. Ask them to notice what they are seeing, hearing, feeling, tasting, and smelling.

Ask them to give their movie a name to use as a Reminder Phrase: Mother laughed; David hit me; the school bully; John scared me. Use a Setup such as "Even though I have this [title] movie, I deeply and completely accept myself." At this point, the client is not telling you about the movie but running it in their head.

Do several rounds of EFT using the name of the movie as a Reminder Phrase. Reassess the emotional intensity after tapping. Repeat until the intensity is 3 or below.

Then ask if there is any part of the overall movie that is most intense – which should have become much less intense as a result of first addressing their concerns about looking at the movie and tapping in a general way on the name of the movie. Focus on the intense aspect for the next tapping Setup and rounds. Continue to tap for each intense aspect (or crescendo in the movie) until the client reports the entire movie is a 0.

Continue to tap for any intensity until the client can run the entire movie without emotion and appears calm. This is a good place to use observational skills as you watch for physiological reactions.

Note: For those of you worried about not being able to find the right words, notice that the Setup can be very simple. The only unique words are the words in the title of the movie or the scene. We can't repeat enough the importance of using the client's words. In fact, let's repeat it again: *Use the clients' words.*

Now encourage them to replay the entire movie attempting to intensify the sights, feelings, sounds, smells, and tastes. This works as a test to see if the client is still upset about the event. Stop and tap at the very first sign of any upset even if it is as low as a 1. People have a tendency to want to "push" through their pain.

Up to this point, the client has been running their movie silently in their head. Now ask if they are willing to tell the story out loud. Stop again at any level of intensity as they tell their story.

You may find that when a client narrates the movie after they believe there is no more intensity, the client is often surprised that other upsetting details come up regarding things they hadn't even noticed before. For instance, Karin Davidson had a client whose stepfather would come into her bedroom at night and lie down with her. After using the Movie Technique, the client reported there was no more intensity on anything in that event. Karin then asked her to narrate the movie one more time. The client used to put a trash can in the way of the door so she'd know when her stepfather entered. When she got to a certain point in the story, she stopped and said, "Oh my! The noise! It's the noise the metal trashcan made! I hate metal trash cans even now. For the last thirty years, I wouldn't have metal trashcans in or around my home! And I have this strange fear that comes up every time I pass close to a metal trashcan. I never realized!"

Each of the three techniques just described involve varying degrees of disassociation of the client from their problem. Tearless Trauma has the client double disassociate and the Movie Technique disassociates. In the case of the Tell the Story Technique, the client associates with the event. The more the client is associated with the story, the more emotion they may feel. The reason you want the client to tell you the story at the end is to make sure that, when they are associated, the emotional intensity is still 0.

When Clients Aren't Telling

The purpose of the Tell the Story Technique is to make sure all the aspects are resolved when the client is fully involved in the story. This is an excellent way to test if you have resolved all the aspects surrounding the story. However, if the client doesn't want to tell you the story, EFT can still resolve the issue. The Movie Technique is first run silently, tapping for any intensity, before the client tells what happened. Your client may choose not to tell the story out loud at all. Respect this choice. Fortunately, the practitioner doesn't have to know the story for EFT to be effective, although telling the story is a good way to test. If the client is not willing to talk about their movie – which is especially common when tapping in public – that's all right; EFT can be effective anyway. You are just not able to test fully for complete resolution on all aspects.

The client being tuned in to the issue while tapping is the critical part for effective tapping. You actually need very little information to use the Movie Technique effectively. For instance, Charlie, an adolescent male resident of a program for emotionally disturbed youth, had been placed on cottage restriction for threatening staff – again. He was not known to be willing to talk about his problems. When Ann Adams worked with Charlie using the Movie Technique, she only asked him how long his movie was, how old he was when it happened, and to choose a color about the movie like red, black, or yellow. Charlie gave only information like: one minute, age twelve, black. He tapped through many different movies that afternoon. He became calmer, stopped being aggressive, and got off restriction. Keep in mind that Ann never knew what he tapped about. She tested by asking if the movie still had a bad feeling to it when he looked back at the movie and paid close attention to what he saw, heard, felt, tasted, and smelled. We do want to test our results with EFT whenever we can. The ultimate "test," however, is the behavior in the future. *We don't really need the content of the story; we only need the client's response to the story.*

Test Your Knowledge

1. What is the purpose of the Movie Technique?

2. True or false? Clients will always go directly to the specific issue.

3. When working with a client's story it is important to:

    a. ignore emotions that surface.

    b. console the client.

    c. tap until the intensity level is significantly diminished.

    d. say all the details out loud.

Answers can be found in Appendix C

Dealing with What Comes Up

High Emotional Intensity

It bears repeating that if you are very upset, just tap without words. You are already tuned in. When the intensity is lower, you can then add in Setups and Reminder Phrases. Tapping without words can actually be preferable if the intensity is very high. Sometimes you may find that the intense issue resolves while tapping without *any* words.

At one of Gary Craig's workshops, a woman in the audience became very emotional. Craig came off stage and just tapped on her over and over and over, tapping the points up and down her body, with no words, until she became calm. This is an example of continuous tapping without words.

Remain Calm

For practitioners: If your client becomes emotionally overwhelmed, it is important for you to *remain calm*. The first time this happens can be frightening to a new practitioner. Stay calm. Clients sometimes become emotionally overwhelmed when they access a very painful memory, especially if they haven't accessed this memory fully in a long time.

This is one of the most important reasons for doing your own work. The more you have worked through your own issues, the more calmly you can respond to another's issues. The more you have done your own work, the less you are "triggered" by your client's stories. Your client may relate an intense, painful, gory, even horrible event. It is sometimes amazing that one human can treat another human, especially a small child, in the ways humans have. If you have not resolved your own deep issues, your unresolved "stuff" can get in the way of helping your client. Without clear boundaries in your own life, you can overreact or be caught up in their story. There are times when you can experience "secondary trauma" from hearing a client story. Always tap after such sessions to clear your own emotional reaction. The problems the practitioner has in dealing with a client invariably reflect the practitioner's unfinished business around his or her own issues. There is no substitute for doing your own work and getting feedback. Having a consultant or mentor to discuss cases and problems is a good idea no matter how much "work" you have done on your own issues. As Gary Craig says, "We are never fully done."

Sometimes the client has never told anyone about the event or has bottled the feelings for a very long time. Now, in using EFT, the client accesses the event, and all the feelings and emotions can come tumbling out at a high intensity. This can also happen if the client has a tendency to keep their emotions locked up. EFT has a way of unlocking that lock. It is important to stay calm. Ask permission to tap on your client. Take their hand and start tapping on the finger and hand points (shown later in this training resource). While you are tapping, explain that it is OK to have that kind of reaction; tell them it is OK to cry and nothing to be ashamed of. Explain that the event is in the past and that they are in the here and now and safe with you.

When the client has calmed sufficiently, you may choose to start tapping EFT points that are non-intrusive such as finger points. Progress to other points as they calm further or have them begin to tap for themselves. Tap afterward for the client's feelings around becoming so upset. Your clients will have feelings around being so emotional: confusion, surprise, shame, and more. On the positive side, when they have worked through the intense issue, they feel very relieved and may have significant cognitive shifts.

When people are fully into a past emotional event, they tend to close their eyes. It is best for them to keep their eyes open to remain in the here and now. Ask them to open their eyes and look at you. You can also choose to "break state" by asking them a question that will necessitate them responding to you about something unrelated to the event. After breaking state, you can start again in a gentler way to approach the issue.

The possibility of an emotional upset is a very good reason for spending some time at the beginning of a session just getting to know your client and establishing good rapport. And all of the previous are very good reasons to continue your EFT learning past level 1.

Deeper Issues May Surface

As you resolve some of the more surface issues, foundational issues may be uncovered. There is the possibility that, after an EFT session, other issues arise between sessions. Be prepared to tap if these new issues or emotions arise unexpectedly. Practitioners should be sure to warn clients of this possibility.

For the most successful results, it is important to make tapping part of your daily routine. Tap several times a day.

Diary Exercise

Create a "tapping schedule" you can follow as you go about your daily activities. Make a list of times that you can tap each day. What are the times and places during the day where you can most easily tap? Write these in your appointment book or diary.

Tapping several times during the day is helpful. The easiest way to remember to tap is to link tapping times to your existing routine. Tap when you get up; tap every time you're in the bathroom; before and after each meal; before you go to bed. Create your own list of daily times to tap. Some people make a checklist and mark off how many times a day they tapped. Play around with what works best for you.

Adding a short tapping routine regularly throughout your day enables you to handle common triggers as they arise. Write down any issues that arise and address these issues when you can tap for longer periods. It's important for you to schedule these longer sessions as well. Whether tapping a few minutes several times throughout the day or planning an appointment with yourself for an hour, be consistent and address your own issues regularly.

Stay in the Here and Now

Often when we are upset, we tend to breathe shallowly. Pay attention to your breathing. Use the Constricted Breathing exercise described in chapter 2 when you notice you are not breathing fully. As a practitioner, when you notice this, you can remind your client to take slow, deep breaths or guide them through the Constricted Breathing exercise. There is some concern that slow deep breaths can trigger an asthmatic attack for those so afflicted. As always, adjust any suggestions to fit your client.

Clients do cry in sessions. Generally, this is a positive release of emotion and lasts only a short time. Sometimes, however, the intensity becomes very high. If you have permission, you can tap on the client over and over (or as Craig puts it, "up and down the body"). As mentioned, if your client does not begin to calm within several minutes or is not responding to continuous tapping, you may choose to "break state." This means that you help the client to be in the here and now. This involves gently saying statements such as "Look at me. You are here with me." If this is not effective, ask a question (or make a request) that would take the person out of the upset state: "Tell me where you are now" or "Tell me how you came here today" or "What color is the carpet?" Use any statement or question that grounds the person in the here and now. You can address their issue more gently and slowly when they become calm again. Your reassuring and calm presence is extremely important in these situations.

Dealing with Clients

Skipping Words

Obviously, not all emotions will be at a high intensity. Since you are working to decrease emotions before the client addresses the issue directly, in most cases you will work with mid- to low-range emotion. In most EFT sessions with practitioners, the client repeats what the practitioner says while tapping the points. Sometimes, though, the client can't say the words because the issue brought up a great deal of emotion. This is normal. The practitioner has to make a decision at these times, based on his or her knowledge of the client and intuition about what is going on. The practitioner can choose to tap without words or continue on, offering tapping words, and the client will join in when it feels possible to do so.

Private Tapping

Sometimes a client cannot or does not want to give you words for their issue. Perhaps you are tapping in a public setting. In these cases, just use a generic phrase such as "This happened." Or you could use a code word or phrase such as "Even though I have this elephant problem, I deeply and completely accept myself."

Nondirective

Sometimes there is emotion without words; we may not even know why we feel the way we feel. Start the Setup and just pause at the problem part, "Even though I [pause] I deeply and completely accept myself anyway." Several Setups like this usually brings up something more specific.

Another useful tool for a practitioner is to begin a sentence then stop and allow the client to fill it in with whatever came up. "I am depressed because ... I don't want to feel anything because ..."

Start Small

This approach is helpful for people who have had their problem for so long that their lives are organized around it. Removing the problem might cause a large disruption in life as they know it. Even the idea that the problem may be removed can create much anxiety. EFT becomes a threat to their very lifestyle. Remember we all have a natural resistance to change. Start with a very small, almost irrelevant, part of the problem. Gwyneth Moss, EFT Master and AAMET trainer, uses this example for an agoraphobic: "Even though I can't even touch the front door handle, I truly and deeply accept myself."

Other clients may need small steps toward the involved event to prevent becoming intensely emotional. You can "sneak up on the problem" by starting slowly; using less intense, more general language in order to decrease anxiety before going to the actual event(s). Using these refinements with clients takes more training and lots of practice. (We encourage you to take another EFT class and read the level 2 training resource.)

No Emotional Response

Working effectively with EFT does not require an emotional charge. EFT still works even if don't feel any intensity. Even without intensity, you do need a tuned-in *awareness* of the incident. Telling the story of the issue or memory generally creates sufficient awareness.

Ask, "What memory do you have that you would rather not have?" Tap for all parts of that memory, whether or not there is emotion. Ordinarily, the memory would not be discussed if there were not still some emotion around it. Tap with all the points (use the entire Full Basic Recipe described in chapter 7 – no shortcuts. As you tap, emotions or additional memories may arise. Clients may let you know they are finished by changing the subject or acting bored. At the next session, test by asking again what memory they would most like to do without. Often, it turns out to be a different memory.

Another helpful way to deal with little or no emotion in a client is to use submodalities to describe their issue. Submodalities are coded representations of what we see, hear, feel, smell and taste, for example: close or far away, hot or cold, color or black and white, loud or muffled, bitter or sweet.

Make It Up

Karin Davidson has her clients "pretend" they have emotion. She says, "You know the ten-year-old you better than anyone else. Make it up. What do you *think* the little boy would feel?" And then she taps with them as they pretend to feel that emotion, even if they say they can't feel it. You can use this for yourself as well when you are having trouble accessing your emotions around an event. Make it up and tap for the pretend feelings. Don't worry if it feels a bit silly.

In one of Gary Craig's onstage demonstrations, he had a client whose breathing was so bad he could not stand up for more than a few minutes. He had been in a concentration camp when he was two years old but had no memory of it. The family never talked about the experience. Gary asked him to make up a story about the event. The client made up a story of how they had escaped from the camp. As he and Gary tapped for the "story," the man's physiology changed. He was able to stand for much longer periods. The story someone makes up is never random; the unconscious always draws its parallels and delivers up the next "piece" for healing. This demonstration is a great example of the power of the mind-body connection and another example that shows it is not the content, but the response to it, that matters.

Using the Physiological Response

Don't know what the problem is? Note where in your body you feel tension. Describe it in as much detail as you can: this dark, stabbing, choking sensation in my throat; this heavy hippopotamus sitting on my chest. You can tap just for the physical response in your body. Tapping for the specific physiological response can be powerful.

Test Your Knowledge

1. True or false? The client must have a big emotional charge for EFT to be effective.

2. Doing my own EFT work is important because_____.

3. If your client (or you when working on your own issues) becomes very emotional, you would:

   a. stop tapping and tell the client to take slow deep breaths.

   b. tell the client that they are doing a good job and to calm down.

   c. take a deep breath yourself, remain calm, and wait until the client is more in control.

   d. remain calm and keep tapping until the emotions regulate.

Answers can be found in Appendix C

EFT for Physical Issues

What you will learn in chapter 5

How to apply EFT steps and techniques for physical issues

When not to use EFT with physical issues

How to use Chasing the Pain

The concept of Borrowing Benefits

What submodalities are and how to use them

Other ways to measure intensity

Using the Color of Pain technique

Testing for aspects

Various other useful techniques

EFT with Pain

EFT has surprising success reducing pain. It is not unusual to see significant reductions in pain in a very short period of time. There are many reports of EFT, used repetitively over time, reducing and even eliminating chronic pain. Even if the pain is not eliminated completely, there are often noticeable reductions in the levels of pain experienced. Why is this?

EFT can eliminate emotional issues underlying the pain – the emotional drivers. EFT reduces the negative emotions associated with the pain, or addresses unresolved emotional issues and traumatic experiences related to the pain. The fact that EFT reduces or eliminates pain highlights the connection between our emotions and our bodies. This connection shows up over and over in EFT sessions. You can tap for an emotional issue and later notice that some physical issue disappeared as well. Alternatively, you can be tapping for a physical pain and an emotional issue becomes less bothersome.

First, do no harm! Unless you are a physician, make sure you have, or your client has, been screened by a medical professional before beginning EFT. Pain can be a symptom of a problem in need of medical attention. For example, an elderly woman and dedicated EFTer fell one evening, hurting her hip. She was able to tap the pain down to a manageable level so she didn't go to the emergency room, but the next morning, the area was still very sore and starting to swell. She called her doctor who sent her to the emergency room where she learned she had a broken hip and needed surgery.

Note: As a practitioner, keep in mind that, in some cases, offering pain management services could be considered practicing medicine. EFT is not a substitute for medical assistance.

Chasing the Pain

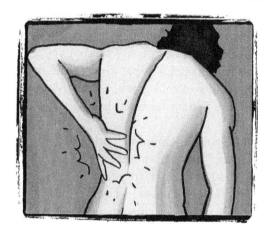

As you tap for your physical pain or discomfort, the experience of pain can change. There can be shifts of the type and quality of pain or the pain can move around. Because of the potential for change, it is important to keep checking as to the type, description, and location of the pain.

In dealing with emotional issues, you look for changing aspects. Is it a new emotion? Is it a new scene in the same event? Have you moved to a related scene or memory? In dealing with physical issues, you are also looking for changes: a change or shift in the type, quality, or location of the pain. Following these changes is called "chasing the pain." Modify the Setup as changes occur.

Clarifying the Pain

Start by identifying the area in your body where the pain is currently most severe. Relief could be as simple as tapping for a clear and specific definition of the pain: "This burning, throbbing ache in my upper shoulders around my trapezius muscles." Generally, however, more than one area needs to be addressed.

Just like finding specifics for an emotional issue, you want to elicit clear specific descriptions of the pain. Emma Roberts, EFT Master, uses the analogy in her classes of sending a letter to a friend. If you address it to Sue Beer in North London, sooner or later it will find its way to Sue. But if you have the specific address and the exact codes, the letter goes straight there. The better you have the exact "address" of the pain, the faster the effects with EFT.

Questions asked can generally be divided into four major areas:

Physical descriptions – where, how bad, specific description. You would ask: "Where is the pain located in your body? What type of pain is it? How severe is the pain? How would you describe the pain?"

Environmental issues – when the pain start started; time, location, or situation in which it is worse. Good questions would be: When did the pain start? What was happening in your life around that time? Does your pain seem to move around the body? Is the pain worse at any particular time of the day? Does it hurt worse in any specific situation?

Emotional reactions – to the pain: anger, frustration, hopelessness, helplessness, and so on. Questions: How do you feel about having the pain? If there were a connected emotional issue, what would it be? If this pain had a message, what would it be?

Related thoughts and/or traumatic events – what happened to cause the pain, what the doctor said, how you were treated, reactions of others, limits to your life, benefits to your life. Questions: What happened to cause the pain? How do the other people in your life respond to your pain? How do you feel about how the medical profession has treated you? What thoughts do you have when you have this pain? What loss is related to your having this pain? What are the losses in self-worth, less activity, less independence? If there were a benefit to you for having this pain, what would it be?

Some descriptions are as *literal* as "This hot, sharp pain in my mid back." Or it may be a more *metaphorical* description such as, "This Mississippi mud pool in my knee." Or *like a character*, "This breathing dragon in my right shoulder." You can tap for *the medical diagnosis*, "Even though I have increased fluid pressure and resulting hardening of my eyeball called glaucoma ..." Or you may choose to address first the feelings *or emotions about the symptom*, "Even though I am so angry that my knee is letting me down ..." Or the *implicit emotion*, "Even though this pain is really angry at something or somebody ..." Or the *personal feelings* about the physical issue, "Even though I am afraid I can't play golf ..." Or "Even though I feel totally stupid for missing the chair ..." (Moss, 2010).

Joe's lower back had been hurting him for years. He'd been to various doctors who said X rays showed he had a slipped disk. The last doctor told him that back pain was often complex, that some people with similar back issues have no pain while others with mild physical issues have intense pain. He told Joe that, because surgery did not guarantee the elimination of pain, he recommended a pain management program before considering an operation. Joe's pain management consultant was well versed in EFT. He asked questions to gather information about the pain and how it affected Joe's life.

Consultant: Where exactly do you feel the pain?

Joe pointed to a specific spot on his back.

Consultant: What type of pain is it?

Joe: A dull ache.

Consultant: How severe is the pain on a scale of 0 to 10?

Joe: Right now a 7. When I rest, it goes down to a 3. When I am overly active, it can go up to a 10.

Consultant: How would you describe the pain?

Joe: As a total nuisance.

Consultant: When did the pain start?

Joe: About ten years ago.

Consultant: What was happening in your life around that time?

Joe: That's about the time my son was born.

Consultant: What happened to cause the pain?

Joe: I twisted in my chair and it tipped over. Something pulled in my back.

Consultant: How do you feel about having the pain?

Joe: Frustrated, but I guess by now I am resigned to the pain.

Consultant: What thoughts do you have when you have this pain?

Joe: I wish I didn't have it, but I don't think there is any thing I can do about it.

Consultant: What loss is related to your having this pain?

Joe: One thing is that I can't play eighteen holes of golf with my buddies anymore.

Consultant:	Is your pain always in the same place or does it some times hurt in another place?
Joe:	Sometimes if I have done a lot of work in the yard, it also hurts a bit higher up.
Consultant:	If there were a connected emotional issue, what would it be?
Joe:	(after looking puzzled and thinking for a few minutes) It would be anger.
Consultant:	If this pain had a message, what would it be?
Joe:	I guess it would tell me I was getting older and shouldn't expect too much from myself.
Consultant:	What benefit is there to you for having this pain?

Joe's reaction to this question was an angry denial of *any* benefit.

Joe's consultant was looking for a tap-able issue. He was searching for a specific event that may have been affecting Joe's back issue. Joe gave the consultant several important clues to specific emotional events that could be related to pain. Joe was angry, frustrated, and felt helpless to change the situation. Because Joe's pain was relatively high at a 7, the consultant decided to use EFT directly for the pain before getting into any emotional issues. He explained that EFT was based on the concepts behind acupuncture, but they would be tapping the acupressure points with fingers instead of using needles. He told Joe that there was research into the effectiveness of these tapping methods, but the technique would still be considered experimental. Joe agreed to give EFT a try. The consultant asked Joe just to follow along and do as he did.

Setup: As they tapped on the Karate Chop point, they repeated the Setup three times: "Even though I have a dull ache in just this spot on my lower back, I deeply and completely accept myself."

Reminder Phrase: They tapped all the Basic Recipe points while saying, "This dull ache."

After three rounds of tapping, the consultant asked Joe if the pain was still a 7. Joe touched his lower back, saying, "I think it is down a bit; maybe a 5."

Joe's face looked less strained. He sat more relaxed in his chair. The consultant asked Joe what came up for him as he was tapping. "It really doesn't have anything to do with my back." The consultant told him it was important to let him know anything that came up as they were tapping, no matter how unrelated it might seem. "Well, I was remembering this time when I was, oh, I don't know, four or five ... when Mom was reading a children's magazine to me on how to make a cardboard car. And after I made it, I took it into Dad's study and he said my model was terrible and to go try again. It *was* terrible, but I was only four."

So the consultant said, "Let's just tap with that." Go ahead and tell me the story again from the beginning and we'll tap while you tell it.

Joe tapped and talked. The consultant asked particular questions as Joe talked: "How did that make you feel?" Joe was simply telling the story until he got to the part where he was opening the door to his father's study. The consultant could see something on Joe's face and asked, "What's happening now?" Joe said, "I forgot that I wasn't supposed to just walk in on Dad while he's working with the door closed. I forgot about that." The consultant then helped Joe to focus on that particular part of his story.

Consultant:	What word would you use to describe that feeling?
Joe:	Ummm ... "better not."
Consultant:	And how strong is that feeling on a scale of 1 to 10?
Joe:	Well, now? I don't care.
Consultant:	If you were that four-year-old again. How strong is the feeling?
Joe:	Well, obviously, I went in ... but, before, I guess it was like an 8.

Note that Joe, as a few people do, denied any current feeling about the event. However, he obviously had some reaction that showed on his face as he got to the part of the story where he opened his father's door. Operating on the assumption that no memory comes up randomly, the consultant then pursued the memory of the intensity, another form of "guessing." They then tapped with "this better-not feeling" until the intensity was a 1. Then the consultant had Joe continue to tell the story and tap. Anytime Joe felt, or showed, intensity at a part of the story, the consultant would stop and ask clarifying questions and tap until the intensity was down to a 1 or 0. The highest intensity was with his dad's response.

Joe:	I can hear his words like it was yesterday ... "Joey, that's terrible. You can do better than that. You must not have been trying. Get out of here and try again." His face was so disappointed.

To Joe's complete surprise, he started to tear up. The consultant did not stop to ask about intensity this time – it was obvious. He just started tapping with Joe for "He was so disappointed." After a few rounds of tapping, the consultant asked how the intensity on the disappointment was now. Joe let out a big sigh and said, "Oh, I don't know ... I don't think he was really disappointed. I think he was just upset I disturbed him. I remember now he was on some kind of project and had stayed up all night."

Consultant: So the disappointment is down?

Joe: Yes, that's what I said ... like a 1 or even not there at all. But he still shouldn't have said it was terrible.

The consultant and Joe proceeded like this until all the emotions around the event were 0. Joe thought it was interesting that he had "forgotten" about the project and his dad being up all night. He said, "Well, no wonder. He was just tired and I barged in on him. Wow ... I just remembered that he came out of the study a bit later and sat down at the table with me and helped me. He even told me I did a good job. I had forgotten all of that."

The consultant noticed that Joe was sitting very comfortably in his chair now, breathing more regularly, and smiling. The consultant had Joe run through the story one more time. "I made a cardboard car and went to show my dad and went in the door anyway even though I knew I wasn't supposed to. That surprised my dad and he'd been up all night for something due that day and said some stuff to me and I took it wrong ... I mean he could've probably said it nicer, but anybody would get caught off guard and could say the wrong thing with no sleep. So I went out and started over and my dad came out and helped me and told me how great an architect I was – did I tell you that my dad was an architect? So I felt really good. Wow, I'm so glad I remembered the rest of the story."

The consultant remembered Joe's response about the birth of his son and asked, "How did you feel about the birth of your son? Is there anything about your father or disappointment?" Joe thought a moment and said, "Oh, I remember looking down at this newborn baby and feeling afraid that I would be a disappointment to him because I didn't know anything about being a father."

They tapped for those feelings and went through the event until all of Joe's aspects were down to a 0. Joe said, "Of course I was nervous! But everything turned out great. And I remember now that my wife and I talked about it and we knew we were a team and could help each other with our wonderful new baby."

The consultant asked about Joe's anger toward his back. Joe thought a few minutes and said, "Well, I *was* angry about that. Actually often ... but I can't feel that right now. It's more sadness because of the wasted time." So they tapped for the sadness until it was a 0. The he asked Joe, "Do you feel helpless about your back?" Joe thought and said, "I'm tired of it, but anyone would be tired of it. I just have to keep trying different things until I can get relief. It's a pain." Joe laughed at his own pun and added, "I mean, here I am tapping on myself, for goodness sake!"

And how's your back, Joe," asked the consultant. Joe answered, "Oh, right now? Well ... what the heck? I wasn't paying attention and it doesn't hurt right now. Wait a second." Joe stood up and bent back and forth a bit, "No, it really doesn't. It's been like ten years since it didn't hurt – and especially when I bend like that."

The consultant told Joe that sometimes we hold pain in our bodies for a reason. Maybe the way his father made him feel and his fear of being a disappointment contributed to the back pain. He also told Joe that they might have to do some more EFT on other times he felt he disappointed people. The consultant told him that he should go back to his doctor to check on the problem even if the pain doesn't come back.

The Color of Pain

EFT Master Paul Lynch regularly uses a technique he calls "the Color of Pain" to develop a specific definition of the pain. He asks his client to give the pain a color and shape.

This method uses submodalities to describe the pain, asking questions like: Where in your body do you feel it? Give it a color. What shape is it? Is it large/small? Heavy or light? Does it have texture? Does it have smooth or ragged edges? Does it make a sound? Is it static or moving? What's in the middle of it? Is it solid or hollow?

Create a Setup from the answers. Example, "Even though I have this black, oval, rock-hard knot under my left shoulder blade, I deeply and completely accept myself."

Note: This technique can also be used if you are unable to get in touch with the emotion attached to your physical issue.

Test Your Knowledge

1. Find a physical issue in your own body (past or present) and clarify it using the techniques you have just learned. Write it out in detail.

2. What question(s) would you not ask in working with physical issues? (Choose one or more answers.)

> *a. How do you feel about having the pain?*

> *b. What is the size, shape, or color of the pain?*

> *c. What do you need to do to increase the pain so we can focus on it?*

> *d. What does having the pain mean in your life?*

Answers can be found in Appendix C

Be Persistent

Sometimes physical issues can take a good while to resolve, and not all physical issues are resolved with EFT. However, perseverance is very important in dealing with chronic, "stubborn" issues. Ann Adams had a pain in her mid back for many years. A constant ache, it never went away. She had tapped for it many times on her own and in Gary Craig's workshops. In a workshop run by Carol Look, Ann tapped once more on her mid-back chronic pain. As she "borrowed benefits" (details follow) from Carol's client, a sudden feeling of rage rose in her toward what her brother-in-law had said to her when her husband died. Ann was surprised, as she did not remember feeling rage at the time her brother-in-law made the comment to her. As the feeling of rage went to a 0, she was even more surprised to find that the mid-back pain was gone. And, as of the date of this printing, it remains gone – over five years later.

Sometimes getting to the core emotion or event behind our pain or physical problem can take a lot of tapping and detective work. EFT Master Andy Bryce tells the story of tapping for six months before his chronic knee pain subsided. Scheduling a few sessions with an experienced EFTer may be helpful in such cases. Be persistent; you may be surprised at what comes up.

Borrowing Benefits

Borrowing Benefits is decreasing the intensity on your own issue as you tap along while watching a session in which another person is working on their issue. You choose an event that, when you think of it, causes you emotional or physical pain or discomfort. You make a mental movie of your event. Give it a name and assess your intensity level, writing it down for reference. Then put it aside. You are not focusing on your event as you watch someone else experiencing EFT – live or on video – and tap along with them. Don't think about or focus on your "movie." Their issue may or may not be related to yours. Just tap as they tap. When they stop to assess their intensity, look at the number you wrote down and then reassess to see if your own intensity level has decreased. Generally, you will experience relief on your own issue. If your number reaches 0, pick another event, make a movie, give it a title, assess the intensity, write it down, set it aside, and continue to tap along with the demonstration.

Note: Tapping along with someone else's issue and using their tapping words will not make you suddenly "catch" their issue. As Bob Doyle explained in his DVD set *Law of Attraction and EFT,* if you tap while saying "I have green skin," your skin won't suddenly turn green (Doyle and Look, 2007). The same is true if you tap along with others' emotions and events. You are tapping with your own energy system and will not "catch" others' problems. EFT practitioners tap daily with others' issues without "absorbing" those issues.

CHAPTER 5 – EFT FOR PHYSICAL ISSUES

Bob sat in the audience as Gary Craig worked on stage with a Vietnam veteran. Bob was new to EFT and had come along with his friend just for a lark. Craig asked the audience to pick a negative issue from their life and tap along with his demo client. Bob picked a negative experience with his father at age twelve. Craig told the audience to write down a code name for the event and what intensity they felt as they thought about it. He then told the audience not to think about it anymore, just to tap along as he tapped with his client.

As Craig's client related his wartime experiences and tapped, Bob tapped along on his father issue. As Craig stopped to check the veteran's intensity, Bob checked his as well. Bob was surprised that the intensity had reduced from a 9 to a 3. When Craig stopped again to check intensity, Bob's intensity had gone to a 0 on the father incident. Bob realized he had moved to an event when he was in the army. The event was related to the father event as both involved verbal abuse toward him. He was surprised to realize after the demonstration that he had resolved four negative events from his own life. He turned to his friend and said, "Gee, this stuff could change my life!"

Things to Notice as You Tap

Behavior, body language, and tone of voice all tell the careful observer much about how someone is feeling. When working on your own issues, pay attention to any changes in your voice, body, or behavior. When you are working alone, however, you may not notice these sometimes-subtle responses; don't worry about it. The important thing is that you are seeing results with your tapping.

One of the most important skills of a good counselor is to establish rapport with the client. A second very important skill is to learn to observe carefully all physical responses the client exhibits and to take careful note of any changes. These give you clues as to how the tapping session is going. Giving feedback to the client on these changes is also helpful in having clients recognize their own progress. The following are areas of observation and some questions to ask yourself to note your client's physical responses:

General physical: How did they walk into the room, how are they sitting, what expression is on their face, are they neat and clean, are they dressed appropriately for the weather?

Movement: How do they move each part of their body? Note things like shifting in chair, eyes darting around, foot or fingers tapping.

Skin: What is the skin tone and color? How are they breathing? Fast, deep, shallow?

Voice: Are they speaking softly or loudly? Do they sound angry, resigned, whiny, etc.?

Measures of Intensity

Testing is an important part of working with EFT. Because EFT can work quickly on a specific event or aspect, you need to test to make sure it is totally gone and there are no more parts or pieces to be addressed. Testing can show you either that all aspects have been addressed and resolved or where you need to do additional work.

Remember that one of the first steps in applying EFT is to decide on a way to test your results. You check your intensity level at the beginning of tapping, check again as you go, and *always* test when you are finished. Generally, EFT uses a 0-to-10 scale of measure (Subjective Unit of Distress, or SUD). There are other tests that may be useful as well.

Percentage

Alternatively, you can use a percentage from 0 to 100 to assess the level of truth or factuality of any statement, as we did with the percentage of a full breath in the Constricted Breathing exercise.

Creative Alternatives

Alternative methods that are a bit more creative can also be useful. The goal of any intensity test is to measure the change or lack of change. Did it change in any way – go up, down, stay the same? If you forget to test before you start, you can start by assuming a level. For instance, say you started tapping and, in the emotion of the moment, you didn't get an intensity level – it happens! Just ask, "If this event were a 10 when I started tapping, what would the number be now?"

A fun way to measure, especially for children, but also useful with adults dealing with childhood issues, is the outstretched hands technique. With this method, a 10 would be as far as your hands can reach to either side of your body and a 0 would have your hands in a prayer position. It's very similar to the "I love you *this* much" scale you may have used as a child.

Metaphors, though not as specific, are also useful. For instance, you can use a traffic light or fire danger sign as a meter: "Is it green, yellow, or red?" A fun one is: "Is the feeling papa bear, mama bear, or baby bear size?" At times, the best you can get is: it's awful, it's better, it's OK now.

Submodalities

Measuring the changes in perception is another way to assess progress. Using submodalities, you can follow the progress as you work on any event by looking at the changes that occur when you picture the event in your mind. More examples of submodalities are: far away versus up close, moving or still, clear or fuzzy, 3-D or flat. Any comparison that helps define the picture can be used.

Test Your Knowledge

1. Describe borrowing benefits.

2. In building rapport with your client, which of the following is unimportant?

> *a. How they hold their body*
>
> *b. Eye contact*
>
> *c. Hairstyle*
>
> *d. Breathing*

3. True or false? There is only one way to measure intensity.

Answers can be found in Appendix C

Testing for Aspects

You've tested to see that there is no more intensity felt and you've resolved what you believe to be all the aspects around an issue. You want to double-check to assure that all parts and pieces and emotions have been covered. Your issue may *feel* complete since the overall issue no longer has any emotional intensity, but since all the involved issues and aspects of issues have to be cleared to alleviate a problem completely, testing for completion is an important part of EFT.

Unresolved aspects or parts and pieces of the issue may make the issue seem to come back; it may then appear as if EFT didn't work. Going back to review each part of the issue ensures that you've addressed all involved parts and pieces. Because you have worked on a specific issue with specific aspects and specific details, it is relatively easy to go back and check on those specifics. This is another reason it's helpful to write down the feeling and the intensity. It makes it easy to go back and check all the aspects.

Sometimes you can clear a specific incident with all its aspects but not feel total relief. What happened? Usually, it's because other related incidents or issues are still affecting the presenting one. A frequently used metaphor is that your problem is like a tabletop. (Cialdini 1998) The specific events and aspects are the table legs holding up that problem. There can be tabletops under the tabletop! Keep looking and tapping for related events that represent the same presenting problem. Level 2 will teach you much more about how to deal with multiple tabletops.

Replay the Event

There are several ways to test your results that use some of the concepts behind the Movie Technique. One creative way to evaluate progress is to go back to the specific event where you started tapping. Replay the event in your head. Try to make the event as bright and colorful and as close as you can. Exaggerate the sounds, the scene, any tastes or smells. Are there any remaining parts that generate an emotional (or physical) reaction? Tap for any response to anything, however small, that remains. The goal is to have the entire event now be totally neutral.

Vivid Imagining

Vivid Imagining, while similar to the event replay, is more like role-play. You use it as a test by reenacting the scene of the original upsetting event as accurately as you can. Try to recreate the setting, the people, the places, the sounds, the smells, the tones, and pitch of the voices. Always stop and tap at any sign of upset and tap until the intensity is 0 on that aspect. With vivid imagining you will also use all your senses, to reenact what you heard, felt, saw, smelled, or even tasted.

In order to facilitate vivid imagining, you might also use objects or pictures that show a similar issue being addressed. Use sounds of the event that were distressing to you. Use clips from movies with scenes that, before tapping, might have been upsetting. For example, a client who has worked to resolve a fear of snakes might be tested with the snake scene in Steven Spielberg's *Raiders of the Lost Ark*.

Future Pacing

Some issues lend themselves to "future pacing." This involves imagining a similar event in the future. For instance, to test for a public speaking phobia, walk through *each* step of delivering a future speech. Start with getting dressed to go to the event, to being introduced, to beginning, then delivering the speech. Move then to the very end, after getting off the stage and seeing people's reactions, to returning home after the event. Stop at *any* point of intensity to tap for even a very small remaining aspect of the fear of public speaking.

Ann Adams gives an example of this in her client Sally who became upset every time her mother called. Her mom complained about anything and everything, and Sally took this to mean she was responsible for fixing her mom's problems. Since Sally couldn't fix all the issues in her mom's life, she felt guilty and as if she had failed as a daughter. Sally tapped for several phone call incidents, which led to a couple of childhood memories about her mother that gave her the same feeling of not being capable. As she dealt with each memory, Sally came to the awareness that while she'd like her mother to be happier, the problems were really because of her mom's perceptions of the world and had nothing to do with Sally's capabilities in the world. Sally now felt compassion, but not responsibility toward her mom. To test if Sally's sense of guilt and failure as a daughter was truly resolved, Ann asked Sally to imagine vividly a future phone call with her mom. She pictured answering the phone, saying hello, listening to her mom complain. She imagined what she would say and how she would deal with the call without becoming upset again. Sally had to tap more as she envisioned what she would say to her mother and imagined her mother's response. Sally continued tapping until she could picture herself remaining respectful and calm throughout the call.

In Vivo

The ultimate test is an actual in vivo (in the situation) test – our real-life responses to previous triggers. You actually give a speech. Sally actually talks to her mother. These kinds of "tests" can bring up aspects that didn't arise while you were tapping. This doesn't mean EFT didn't work. It just means there are a few more hidden aspects to tap for.

In Gary Craig's seminars, he was famous for coming up with in vivo tests. One of Craig's subjects was afraid she wouldn't be able to explain EFT. After dealing with the issues, Craig found a willing volunteer from the hotel staff, who knew nothing about EFT. Craig's demo subject explained EFT skillfully to the staff person. In another example, he had a woman who said she was too embarrassed ever to dance with a man dance with Craig at the break. Carol Look, EFT Master, worked on stage at an EFT Master Showcase with a woman who had studied EFT thoroughly but still had a fear of not being able to do an EFT session. After successfully dealing with the woman's issues around her fears, Carol had the woman be the "practitioner" and do a short session with Carol as "the client," still on stage.

Whenever possible, *after tapping through all the aspects* around your issue, test it in vivo:

- If you were upset every time your mother called, call your mother.
- If you were afraid of mice, go see a mouse at a pet store.
- If you were afraid of public speaking, give a speech.
- If you were upset every time you read the goodbye letter from your girl-friend, read it again.

The truth is, until you experience the calmer you in the real world, you don't really know that you are finished with the issue. The world around you is the best teacher for helping you get in touch with your emotions and issues – and any unfinished aspects.

Is There Anything Else?

When one event is resolved, you can find out if there are other similar events. Are there earlier experiences that are related? A perfect question at the end of each tapping round to check for additional aspects is: "What comes up for you now?"

Aspects Lead to Connected Events

When possible, it's useful to ask if a person remembers a similar event or a time when they felt the same emotion. *Can you remember another time when you felt the same way?* Karin Davidson refers to these related incidents as nodules on an "issue string." Karin's client Kathy had a terrible sense of physical self. She was embarrassed to undress in front of her husband and couldn't bring herself to go to a public gym or swimming pool. She reported that she had felt this way for as long as she could remember. As she grew up, there were *many* events in which this embarrassed feeling occurred.

An issue string is first formed with the occurrence of a specific event containing UDIN (*Unexpected, Dramatic, Isolating,* and you have *No strategy* to deal with it). A response or learning occurs, and when other events happen, these additional events confirm or reinforce the response, learning, and belief created at the first event. Therefore, Karin continued to try to find the *first* time her client felt that same feeling. She wrote down the events Kathy mentioned – all the nodules on this issue string. As she was remembering events, Kathy remembered changing for gym class in school when she was seven and someone teased her about her birthmark. The intensity of that was a 10, so Karin and Kathy used the Movie Technique to clear that event. Karin then asked Kathy again, "When was the *first* time you can remember feeling those same feelings." As she was thinking, Kathy paused and then said, "Never mind." Since anything that comes up is related to the issue at hand, Karin asked what just happened. "Oh, nothing. This weird thing happened with my uncle when I was little," she said. "It really was nothing. My uncle opened the door while I was going to the bathroom and he stared at me a minute and then shut the door," she explained. "How did that make you feel?" Karin asked. Kathy replied, "I didn't feel anything. It was just creepy. No big deal." Karin tapped with Kathy on "this creepy feeling." And Karin said, "Did you feel anything else?" Kathy started to say something and a shocked look came over her face, "I just remembered feeling so self-conscious. I didn't want anyone ever to look at me again," and she started to tear up. They used the Tell the Story technique to address all the feelings around that event.

To test if the issue was complete, Karin asked, one by one, about the other events she had mentioned. Kathy reported that they didn't seem important anymore. This is another example of the Generalization Effect. By collapsing the foundational event, all the other "embarrassment" events collapsed as well.

Karin asked how Kathy would feel right now if her husband walked in on her changing, "How would you feel? Would that same feeling come back?" Kathy laughed, "Of course not. That's interesting. It's different. I mean, he's my husband and he loves me. He tells me I'm beautiful all the time. But ..." Karin asked her to explain. "But I'm still so worried about getting old." To Karin, this simply meant a different but related issue string, another tabletop under a tabletop.

Homework

When you have worked through a fear, phobia, or event and can't test it in vivo at the time, make it a goal during the coming week to find a way to confront the fear, phobia, or event that you believe you have resolved.

Test Your Knowledge

1. What is the importance of having the client find the first time they remember the feeling?

2. True or false? Small events are usually not significant.

3. Testing "in vivo" means:

    a. doing the very behavior that was problematic before the EFT session.

    b. practicing on someone else.

    c. using EFT to work on an event that occurred in the womb.

Answers can be found in Appendix C

EFT for Cravings

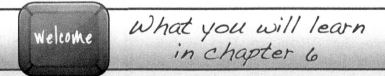

Welcome

What you will learn in chapter 6

How to use EFT to help ease cravings

Addictions as compared to cravings

How adding tapping in your daily routine is helpful

What is addiction really? Craig's view is that we've traditionally had very little success treating them because we haven't really understood the cause of addiction. We've treated it like a bad habit or an inheritance from a troubled parent, for instance. Craig's EFT Manual discusses what addiction is not and finally adds "the true cause of all addictions is anxiety, an uneasy feeling that is temporarily masked, or tranquilized by some substance of behavior." (Craig, 2011, p. 138). In other words, addiction is actually a solution to a problem. Addiction is considered a problem, but it is not "the problem" to tap for. Instead, we look for the underlying problem that the addiction seemingly "solves."

EFT gives an alternative to the need to tranquilize the anxiety caused by underlying strong emotions and negative experiences. Until the underlying reasons for the addiction are addressed, the addictive behavior remains because the reasons for it are still there. At times, a person who gives up one addiction simply switches to another. For instance, when Danny gave up smoking, he increased the amount of beer he drank each night. Only after he worked through his anger at his parents and his extremely low self-esteem was he able to give up the need for any addictive substance. Until the emotionally troubling memories that create the anxiety are resolved, the cravings and other addictive behaviors or substance abuse continues.

Although one-minute wonders do sometimes happen when working with an addiction, generally, addictions are very, very complicated. Discovering the "problem" (i.e., the core issues behind the addiction and specific events leading to the issue) and then dealing with the fears of giving up the solution and resolving reversals can take some time and serious detective work.

EFT does an excellent job of addressing the cravings – strong or mild – that go along with any addiction. Reducing the intensity of the craving to a manageable level gives the person a choice. As long as the intensity is very high, the person is driven to the addictive behavior in an attempt to reduce that intensity. Why? Because it works! The addictive behavior and substances are the person's solution. EFT can give that person another option.

Note: Dealing with actual addictions is beyond the scope of this training resource and level 1. Advanced EFT training and, in some cases, professional training is necessary to use EFT for the addiction itself. Consistent tapping for every craving has been shown, however, to impact addictive behavior. In level 1, we will practice using EFT for cravings.

Using EFT with Cravings

Let's use an example of working with cravings. Debbie loves to have a chocolate candy bar for a snack. The problem is she eats one at the morning break, another after lunch, another at the afternoon break, and sometimes another on the way home from work. She buys them in bulk to make sure she always has one available. Debbie notices her clothes are getting tighter, so Debbie decides to try this new EFT thing.

As with any other problem or issue, it's important to get specific about the craving. When Debbie thinks about the last chocolate bar she ate, she begins to salivate and wants to go get another one. She identifies her chocolate bar craving at a 7 and decides to try tapping.

She closes her eyes and pays attention to what she is thinking and feeling. She feels the craving as "warmth in her stomach." She is thinking about how the chocolate bar tastes when she takes the first bite. She loves the taste of it melting in her mouth. Because that's the strongest feeling, she decides to use the taste of it melting in her mouth as a good place to start. She says the Setup three times: "Even though I love the taste of the chocolate as it melts in my mouth, I deeply and completely accept myself."

She uses "melting chocolate" as her Reminder Phrase. Since she is working on her craving on her own, she decides she won't take any shortcuts and taps all of the meridian points including the fingers, the liver point, and the 9 Gamut (explained in the next chapter). Because she is at a high level of intensity, she decides to do three entire sequences before she stops to measure her intensity again.

When she stops, she is surprised to see that her craving is at a 3. She feels she could eat the chocolate, or not – it is not a big deal. Debbie decides to see if she can get the craving down lower. She notices that now she is thinking about the sweet smell of the chocolate bar before she eats it. She recognizes that this is another aspect; it's no longer about the melting of the chocolate in her mouth.

Debbie changes her Setup: "Even though I love the sweet smell of the choco-late, I deeply and completely accept myself." She taps another three rounds on all the points, including the 9 Gamut. This time she uses the Reminder Phrase "sweet smell." When she finishes, she checks her intensity. It is now barely a 1. She decides to test this with a real candy bar. She gets a candy bar from her desk drawer and unwraps it. She finds she has no desire to eat it. She sniffs the candy bar. Odd, she thinks, it doesn't seem to smell sweet at all; it smells like chemicals. She puts the bar back in her drawer and gets on with her day. She "forgets" to eat the chocolate bar at break.

As cravings are reduced to 3 or below, it becomes a choice to eat the chocolate, or not. At a 7 or higher, it is much harder to resist the substance or behavior.

Will Debbie's Craving Come Back?

Sometimes tapping for a craving is a "one-minute wonder" and it never comes back, but, more likely, persistence will be needed to keep the cravings away until the core issues behind the cravings are resolved. The goal of EFT is to give you a choice. Debbie now has a choice. She can choose to tap whenever she has a crav-ing. Over time, the cravings decrease or are eliminated. The craving can return *if* something happens in her life that triggers any of the unresolved issues behind her craving for chocolate. Remember, addiction is an attempt at a solution to a problem, not the problem itself.

When Is It Most Effective to Tap for a Craving?

Anytime you think about it.
Anytime you think about anything that leads to thinking about it.
Anytime you see someone else doing it.
Anytime you want it.
Anytime you've had it.
Anytime after you've had it.
Anytime you are having feelings about having it.
Anytime.

When is it *least* effective? When you are in the car on your way to the grocery store to pick up ice cream, or walking quickly to the corner deli for a brownie. The chances are that you are *not* going to stop and tap. In these cases, the decision has been made. *Could* you stop and tap for the craving? Of course, but it's much harder to tune in for the craving when you are already focused on the act of going to get the thing you are craving.

Karin Davidson had a client who used cocaine. This particular client didn't have an addiction. He simply turned to cocaine on occasion. The session began with tapping for the craving itself because the client called when he recognized the craving had begun and reached out for help.

After the craving lowered using EFT, Karin asked "When is the point of no return; when can you still say no? At what point is there no backing out of using the cocaine?" After a bit of thought, he said, "Calling my dealer is the point of no return." Karin gave him suggestions on things to tap for when he desires the cocaine and *before* he calls his dealer. The timing for the tapping was crucial. Two years later, the client told Karin that he had not used cocaine since the session because he recognizes that he must tap *before* he calls his dealer.

Although this was resolved in one session, it's important to note that this person did not have a true addiction to cocaine. He used cocaine as a temporary solution to stressful situations. Using EFT to resolve addiction is much more involved. Here, EFT was used to give someone the opportunity of choice.

Cravings are one of the few things you tap about that generally need repetitive tapping until you deal with the root cause (which can be complex). Often, addictions are held in place by multiple, sometimes contradictory beliefs and complex emotions. Tapping for the cravings in the meantime can cut down on cravings, relieve anxiety, and decrease the use of the substance or behavior.

Craving Exercise

Pick a craving you have. Say you love chocolate or salty potato chips or a glass of wine. Get a sample of your favorite. Put it in front of you. Look at it, smell it, take a tiny bite or drink of it. Identify what you best like about it. For example, is it the smell? The first taste of it? The feelings it brings up in you? Get a baseline measurement. How badly do you want the substance, right now, on a scale of 0 to 10? And what exactly is causing the highest intensity?

Like Debbie, decide what is the most appealing to you about the substance and develop a Setup. "Even though [the strongest appeal of this substance] is […], I deeply and completely accept myself anyway."

Tap through all the points at least three times, using the reminder phrase that represents the strongest appeal of your substance. Check your intensity level again. If it is not to a 0, modify the Setup to: "Even though I still have some of this remaining [...], I deeply and completely accept myself anyway." Remember that if you have moved to a different aspect of the substance, modify the Setup to match it.

If the desire has not gone down much, try tapping for resistance or conflict to giving it up. Tap for a few rounds on all points and see what comes up.

"Even though I don't really want to give up my chocolate bar because [...], I deeply and completely accept that is how I feel now."
"Even though part of me wants to keep eating the chocolate bars and part of me wants to stop, I deeply and completely accept both parts of me."

Use EFT for all the aspects and all the feelings that make the substance attractive.

Test Your Knowledge

1. How can EFT address cravings?

2. Select the best time to tap for a craving:

    a. when thinking about the substance

    b. while enjoying the substance

    c. on your way to purchase the substance

    d. after you've had the substance

    e. all of the above

3. True or false? There is no difference between a craving and an addiction.

Answers can be found in Appendix C

The Full Basic Recipe

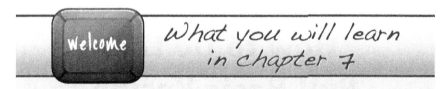

What you will learn in chapter 7

The original Full Basic Recipe

More tapping points

The 9 Gamut Procedure and why it was developed

Learning Additional Points

Although Gary Craig most often used the Basic Recipe (the shortcut version) in his later demonstrations, his introductory manual, which was downloaded by over a million people, taught the full EFT sequence: the Full Basic Recipe. EFT started out as a simplified version of TFT. The Full Basic Recipe used all the TFT points in one algorithm and kept the TFT process of: tapping, then the 9 Gamut Procedure (explained later), and tapping. Craig felt the Basic Recipe (seven points) was as effective as the Full Basic Recipe and rarely used the Full Basic Recipe after his first set of DVDs. Occasionally, however, he would use the finger points and the 9 Gamut depending on the response of his client. Most practitioners now use the Basic Recipe and only add in other points and the 9 Gamut when movement is slow.

Some practitioners continue to use the Full Basic Recipe, however, because they claim to see the client's intensity reduce faster and noticed the client go into deeper issues with better results when using the full version as opposed to the Basic Recipe. Though there has been no research to date on whether the Full Basic Recipe works better, or faster, than the Basic Recipe, using the Full Basic Recipe is recommended when you are not getting fast results with the Basic Recipe. Apparently, some situations do call for using more acupressure points.

Reminder: There are now many alternative techniques using various acupuncture points to help people resolve physical and emotional problems. All of them claim to be effective. EFT is one of the easiest to learn and use for oneself and is the method most often used, up to now, in research on the effectiveness of tapping.

You've already learned some of the points used in the Full Basic Recipe. The Full Basic Recipe starts with the Basic Recipe points. The Full Basic Recipe addresses thirteen meridian points instead of just seven. It also uses an exercise developed by Callahan called the 9 Gamut Procedure (which covers the fourteenth meridian point used in EFT). The 9 Gamut uses eye movements and other exercises designed to impact the brain and reinforce new learning.

How to Do the Full Basic Recipe

Whether you are using the Full Basic Recipe or the shorter Basic Recipe, the process is the same, with three main parts:

1. *Clarification* – Develop a specific description of your issue, preferably a specific event [the time when...] and check the intensity you have *right now* around that event on the 0-to-10 scale or decide on an alternative method for assessing the intensity.

2. *Setup* – Create a problem statement from your issue that is linked to an acceptance statement that you will say while tapping on the Karate Chop point (side of the hand) or the Sore Spot. Repeat the Setup three times. For example, "Even though I have this [problem], I deeply and completely accept myself."

3. *Tapping* – Create and use a Reminder Phrase while tapping on the points in the sequence. The sequence in the Full Basic Recipe is a bit different from a round in the shortcut version. After tapping through the sequence, reassess your intensity, adjust the Setup as needed, and repeat the sequence if the intensity is above a 0.

This three-step process is the same. The difference is in the tapping part. In the Full Basic Recipe, you use more points, you add the 9 Gamut procedure, and tapping becomes a "sandwich" routine. You tap the full series of points (the top slice of bread), you do the 9 Gamut (the filling), and you tap the full series of points again (the bottom slice of bread).

The Process

After clarifying the issue, assessing the intensity, and saying the Setup three times, you begin tapping the points. The Full Basic Recipe points start off the same as the Basic Recipe points. The Full Basic Recipe then adds six additional points. The majority of these additional points are located on your hand. You then do the 9 Gamut Procedure and again tap the thirteen Full Basic Recipe points (fourteen, counting the head point).

Reminder: Though the top of the head point is not in the Full Basic Recipe as described in *The EFT Manual, Sixth Edition,* we have added it, as Gary Craig most often used it in his demonstrations and most practitioners also use it.

The Points

H   – Top of head (some practitioners use this point as the last point rather than the first)

EB – Eyebrow

SE – Side of Eye

UE – Under the Eye

UN – Under the Nose

Ch – Chin (under the lower lip, in the crease)

CB – Collarbone

UA – Under the Arm

Now the Full Basic Recipe goes on to tap these additional points:

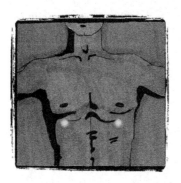 

BN – Located an inch Below the Nipple. This is a liver meridian point.

Th – The side of the fingernail opposite the rest of the hand in the curve of the nail on the Thumb

IF – The body side of the fingernail in the curve on the side of the Index Finger

MF – The body side of the fingernail in the curve on the side of the Middle Finger

BF – The body side of the fingernail in the curve on the side of the Baby Finger

KC – The fleshy side of the hand. *Note:* The Full Basic Recipe ends with tapping the KC just as you would tap any other point.

Because of the difficulty, especially for women, to tap the actual "Below Nipple" or liver meridian point, this point is often skipped, usually with no loss in results. Some practitioners, however, consider this point critical to full success. Often they use a liver meridian point lower on the liver meridian, which appears to work equally well. This point is about a palm's width below the nipple point and out toward the side of the body about two finger lengths.

The 9 Gamut Procedure

After tapping through the thirteen points (fourteen, if you add the head point), you do the 9 Gamut Procedure. Use either hand and locate the Gamut point in the little indentation on the back of your hand just down from where the ring finger and the baby finger join. This indentation (1/2 to 1 inch from the crease where the fingers join) is the Gamut point.

While you are doing the nine steps, look straight ahead, hold your head level, and tap continuously on the Gamut point. Even if you feel a bit silly, continue through the nine steps, as follows:

1. Close your eyes.
2. Open your eyes.
3. Look hard down right to the floor while still holding your head straight ahead.
4. Look hard down left to the floor while sill holding your head straight ahead.
5. Roll your eyes in a circle. Imagine a very large clock on the wall and you are looking at each number in order.
6. Roll your eyes in a circle in the opposite direction, look at each number in the opposite order.
7. Hum about two seconds of any song or melody.
8. Count from one to five very fast.
9. Hum about two seconds of any song or melody again.

The Full Basic Recipe Steps in Detail

First, create your Setup, assess your intensity, and tap the Karate Chop point (or rub Sore Spot) while saying three times your individualized version of "Even though I have this [problem], I deeply and completely accept myself."

Second, begin tapping just as you have in the Basic Recipe, but add all the points as listed for the Full Basic Recipe here. Notice as you tap that all the tapping points continue down the body. Though a major difference between Callahan's TFT and Craig's EFT is that, in EFT, the specific order of the points tapped is not considered important, it is helpful when you are learning the points to follow the down-the-body order. This creates a routine that is easy to follow even when you are feeling stressed.

Third, do the 9 Gamut. This nine-step procedure has been dropped by many practitioners. It is harder to describe and teach someone, and it does look a little strange to an observer.

You may ask why bother with the Full Basic Recipe when the Basic Recipe works well? People are individuals. We never know for certain how well the tapping will work in every possible situation. Adding in the full tapping points and the 9 Gamut Procedure is like insurance. You are covered when you need it. Once you've learned the new points and the 9 Gamut Procedure, adding the extra points and the 9 Gamut takes approximately twenty seconds longer than the shorter Basic Recipe – only 20 seconds!

Sometimes the 9 Gamut is the only thing that moves the issue forward. Mary Sise,LCSW, D.CEP, past president of ACEP, in a correspondence with the authors, described the usefulness of the 9 Gamut:

> In a traumatic event, the eyes widen and the brain freezes. (This is where the deer-in-headlights phrase comes from.) The person's vision narrows, and time expands. The brain goes into survival mode and, due to a flood of chemicals, it does not process the event the way it would if it wasn't traumatic. Brain researchers also believe that the eye movements in our REM sleep state are what allow us to process the events of the day, and release them. It is thought that one of the reasons our sleep is disturbed after a traumatic event is because, as chemicals are released during frightening dreams, we wake up, interrupting the normal processing of events.

> What does this have to do with energy psychology and the 9 Gamut? Well, the eyes are the part of the brain on the outside of the body. *Each time you move the eyes, or open and close them, you are activating a different portion of the brain. When you hum, count, and hum, you activate the right, left, and then right hemisphere.* So, it is quite possible that this 9 Gamut protocol assists the brain in processing the event. It is not unusual for a client to report that when the eyes looked to the right or left (locations can be different for each client or various issues), there was a shift and a release.

The 9 Gamut Procedure is often described as a brain balancing exercise to balance the left and right hemispheres of the brain. Callahan, who developed it, says, "The theory behind the gamut treatments is that we are balancing various functions of the brain with each treatment in regard to the particular problems we are treating. Each problem needs to be treated separately. It is as if the brain must be tuned to the right frequency for each problem for the treatment to work" (Callahan, 1985, p. 15).

When Ann Adams worked with the traumatized children in the residential program, she often used the 9 Gamut Procedure. Her logic was that if this exercise was meant to help balance the brain and help the brain process the new learning created by tapping, these children could certainly use this boost. And the children like the exercise.

Fourth, again tap all thirteen points (plus the head, if you like). End with the Karate Chop point. (Do not repeat the 9 Gamut Procedure after the second round of tapping.)

Fifth, reassess your intensity. Modify the Setup as necessary, just as when using the Basic Recipe, and repeat the steps until your specific event issue is resolved. Remember that you are "sandwiching" the 9 Gamut Procedure between two sets of tapping.

Sixth, as with any tapping protocol, test the results.

The Significance of the Gamut Point

The Gamut point is on Triple Warmer meridian. According to Donna Eden, author of the book *Energy Medicine*, "Triple Warmer is the energy system that maintains existing survival strategies, whether effective, outdated, or completely dysfunctional. It resists efforts to change neural pathways that play an apparently protective function, even those that maintain irrational fear, anger, jealousy, or other emotional responses that are not adaptive or appropriate to the circumstances. Triple Warmer has a strong relationship with each of the other meridians and, under conditions of threat or perceived threat, it usually has a dominating relationship *over* them. In EFT, you tap on the gamut point, which sends calming signals through the Triple Warmer system, at about the same time as you tap on other acupuncture points that send signals that can change outmoded neural and energetic pathways. As Triple Warmer is calmed, it relaxes its hold on the established habit, and deep changes in survival strategies are then able to occur." (personal communication, 2011).

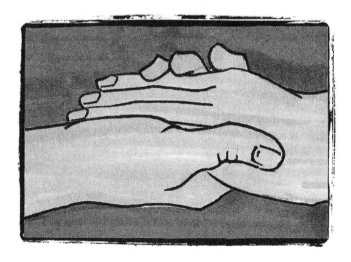

Some EFT practitioners who tap on their clients, use their thumb to lightly press on the Gamut point while using the other hand to tap the points on their clients.

Why Is the Ring Finger Skipped?

The edge of the nail of the ring finger and the Gamut point address the same meridian. It doesn't hurt anything to include the ring finger, but it is not necessary because tapping on the Gamut point is taking care of the balancing on that meridian. Ann had the children in the residential program tap all of their fingers since it was easier for them to tap them all instead of remembering to skip one.

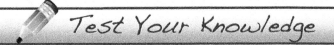

Test Your Knowledge

1. True or false? The three basic steps in the Basic Recipe and the Full Basic Recipe are different.

2. True or false? The 9 Gamut Procedure was developed to balance extreme emotions.

3. What are the steps in the 9 Gamut Procedure?

Answers can be found in Appendix C

Blocks to EFT

What you will learn in chapter 8

What to do when EFT works slowly or not at all

What hidden core issues are and how to deal with them

Bumps in the EFT road

Addressing core issues and negative beliefs

The effect of toxins

The importance and how to do the Personal Peace Procedure

When EFT Works Slowly or Not at All

Let's look at some of the many varieties of "bumps in the road." Each individual case may be slightly different. In skilled hands, EFT can be effective with at least some part of most issues. These results may not be achieved by everyone who uses EFT, however. Additional learning and more practice equals higher skill level. This section describes some of the most common problems people run into when using EFT.

More Details on Reversals

The mechanism that causes our natural energy flow to become blocked or reversed due to trauma, illness, shock, or subconscious sabotage is still unknown.

Goodheart and Callahan noted that, during muscle testing, a client's muscle sometimes responded positively (held strong) when it should have responded negatively (gone weak) and vice versa. They also noticed that when such muscle testing results were reversed, the tapping sequences were not effective. It was necessary to clear such "reversals" before they could proceed. There have been a variety of names for reversals: polarity switching, over energy, energy reversal, and neurological disorganization. For more information about the various types of reversals, see Fred Gallo's book, *Energy Diagnostic and Treatment Methods*.

Some practitioners give the issue of reversals a great deal of emphasis; others feel that reversals are like any other problem to be resolved. Some practitioners (including the authors of this book) tend to focus on the psychological reversals that sabotage our lives. These include issues such as safety, deservedness, secondary gains, and identity issues. Reversals need only be addressed if EFT is not effective. The Setup is designed to correct most reversals, at least long enough for a few sequences of EFT to be used to address the issue.

Not Being Specific

Much time has been spent in this training resource giving you tools to get to a specific. Most likely, the first thing you should ask when EFT is not working is: "Am I working on a *specific* issue?" Are you being too global or generic? Probe deeper. Ask more questions. Find and create a movie of the event. Pick one scene in that movie. Use all five senses. Describe the scene in detail – the smells, sights, sounds, looks on people's faces, colors. Look at the environment around the issue. Is there anything else in the scene that could be affecting the intensity level? What were you thinking? What were you feeling? Be sure you use your (or your client's) actual words in the Setup. Sometimes the words are not "pretty." No time to get squeamish. One therapist got nowhere with a boy who still "messed" his pants in school until he used the boy's words, "Even though I shit my pants in school ..."

Missing Shifting Aspects

People often change aspects as they are tapping. As one issue is resolved, they go on to another. Since it all seems the same problem to them, they continue to give high intensity numbers. Check out what the picture in your (or your client's) head is each time. Remember the story of Gary's roofer client who was afraid of heights? Again, never assume that the picture in your mind is the same as the picture in your client's. In fact, *never assume that you know anything about your client's perceptions, beliefs, and responses*. Always stay curious.

Ask questions to check that you are dealing with the same issue. Did the scene you are seeing change? Are the smells and tastes the same? Are you experiencing the same physical feeling? Is it now a different voice, words, sound?

Complex issues can have multiple aspects. Aspects can move to a new emotion or scene in the same event, or to a related scene or memory. Are you working on the same emotion? Is this a different thought than we started with? Is this a different event?

Sometimes What You Need Is "More"

- Put *more feeling* into the Setup. Say it like you really, really mean it. You may need a much stronger Setup. Try saying it very loudly. One article in Craig's case studies archive was from a woman who could not make any progress on her ice cream addiction until she screamed her Setup.
- You may need *more points*. If you are using the Basic Recipe, use the Full Basic Recipe including the 9 Gamut Procedure.
- You may need *more time*. Tap longer on each point.
- You may simply need to *tap more*. Tap *more often*. Tap for *longer periods* of time.
- You may need *more variety*. Tap at different locations and at different times of the day. *Persistence pays.* Keep tapping.
- Your client may need *more human touch,* meaning you may need to tap *on* your client. Being touched by another can be very therapeutic in and of itself. Naturally, you explain what you plan to do and ask permission to touch your client.

Good rapport is always needed for permission to tap on the person. Craig generally tapped *on* his clients. Most, but by no means all, EFT practitioners tap *with* and not *on* their clients. Though it is rare that tapping on your client is what is needed for EFT to be effective, this is occasionally the case. Then, too, there are times when clients cannot tap for themselves (whether too upset or physically unable). In these cases, *always* ask permission before you begin to tap on them.

Having another person's energy involved in working on your issue can sometimes make all the difference. For self-help, you can choose to have someone tap on you while you say the words silently in your head. You can also choose to share the issues as you tap.

Test Your Knowledge

1. The easiest way to address reversals is to:

   a. ask about any allergies.

   b. use energy work protocols.

   c. divide all issues into simple or complex.

   d. use the Setup.

2. True or false? Three reasons EFT may appear not to work are missing aspects, not being specific enough, and lack of persistence.

3. True or false? Working on your own issues helps you become a better EFT practitioner.

Answers can be found in Appendix C

Hidden Core Issue

Core issues are made up of our beliefs, conclusions, or limitations, or decisions we made from things that happen to us. These conclusions/beliefs/decisions are made during one pivotal event, after a group of events. When we can find the underlying event(s) in which we created the core issue that contributes most to the problem, we can resolve the core issue and move on in our lives. Often core issues are formed in childhood, generally related to authority figures in our lives or from a traumatic experience of some type. We create a variety of ways to cover or hide these issues – because they are painful. We erect ways to protect ourselves. We develop our unique ways of looking at the world. We create an additional problem; the traumatic event is joined by the limiting conclusion we made about ourselves and/or the world.

Good questions are generally necessary to dig out the core issue behind a problem. Core issues are not always obvious; they are often hidden. Finding that core or root problem is important to resolving a difficult case. Keep questioning and prodding until you discover the main cause of a problem. This is not always simple or easy. (EFT level 2 covers this topic in more depth.) Important questions to ask are:

- When did the problem start?
- What was going on when it started?
- Every time you think of your asthma, what else pops into your mind? ("Could the time my brother was killed in that automobile accident really have to do with my developing asthma?" It certainly can. Our bodies find very creative ways to deal with trauma and difficult situations.)
- What does this issue remind you of?

- When was the first time you can remember feeling the same kind of feeling?
- If there were a deeper emotion underlying this problem, what might it be?
- If you had your life to live over, what one person or event would you just as soon skip?

You (or the client) may answer, "I don't know." In these cases, tell yourself (or the client) just to guess or to make up a story as to what it could be. Whatever guesses are made or imaginative story is told is usually *very* relevant.

The problem is not always what we think the problem is. Are you not getting anywhere on an event with strong emotion? Describe the location. Who was there? Describe the expressions on their faces. Describe their tones of voice. Again, use all five senses. EFT Master Lindsay Kenny tells the story of an elderly client working on a scene in which his mother slapped him at the dining room table. As they worked on reducing the emotion around his mother slapping him, the intensity wasn't reducing. It wasn't until Kenny had him describe who was at the dining room table when the slap occurred that he remembered his grand-mother's face. He had looked to her for sympathy and he saw, what as a child he interpreted as, disgust and disappointment at how he handled the slap. Since he adored his grandmother, he was crushed by her reaction even more than by his mother's slap.

Often we just don't want to look at our deepest, most painful, sensitive issues! We don't want to go where we don't want to go. It's logical. Why should you dredge up a painful event when your entire experience to date says it will just hurt? And why bring it up if you think, "It's in the past. It's over. I've handled it." This may be a time to schedule a couple of sessions with an experienced practitioner. As Lindsay Kenny, EFT Master and AAMET trainer, says, dealing with these kinds of issues yourself may be like a dentist trying to pull his or her own teeth.

Strong Negative Beliefs

There are often themes behind our core issues. These are themes we see frequently:

- I am not lovable.
- I am not good enough.

Others show up at times in the language. Listen for the negative self-beliefs or conclusions behind your own or your client's comments: I'm not capable; I'm not smart enough; I don't fit in; I am only valuable if I ...

Listen for the absolutes: I can't do *anything* right; I *always* do the wrong thing; I *always* get rejected; I *never* get chosen for the good jobs.

People often have fears around safety. Listen for safety issues, which people express in many ways, including: I can't; it's not safe to ...; my partner would be upset if I ...

Anger can turn out to be a reaction to one too many rejections, a fear that you don't deserve to be loved. Anxiety can turn out to be a major fear of not measuring up in some way. Depression can turn out to be a deep belief that you are not valuable. Keep asking questions and digging until you uncover what is the driver behind the problem.

Many of us live with unrealistic feelings of shame and guilt stemming from events when we were children. We may still feel childhood rejection. The judgments about ourselves we made when we were six are still playing out today. As adults, we are still listening to the wisdom of a six-year-old. We still feel out of control in our lives – a deep sense of fear that we cannot safely navigate the world. No wonder we respond with anger, controlling behaviors, resentment of authority, helplessness, depression, or addictions.

You've heard the saying, "We spend the rest of our life getting over our childhood!" Fortunately, EFT can expedite the process.

Safety and Deservedness

Another way of looking at major themes that tend to block our progress is a list of common limiting beliefs created by Fred Gallo (2000):

- Deservedness – I don't deserve to get over this.
- Safety – It is not safe for me to get over this. Or, not safe for others ...
- Benefit – There is no benefit to me in getting over this. (Secondary gains.) Or, no benefit to others or could harm others.
- Deprivation – I will be deprived of ... if I get over this.
- Identity – This is who I am. I won't be me if I get over this. (Often totally unaware of this.)
- Lack of forgiveness – That means they got away with it. Or I *am* guilty; I have no right to get over this.
- Looping – I have to have this before I can ... I can't be ... *until* I have this.
- Motivation – I won't do the necessary to get over this.
- Possibility – It is not possible for me to get over this.

Addressing these issues could be as simple as a Setup such as, "For whatever reason I don't want to resolve this problem, I deeply and completely accept myself." Or "Even though I really don't want to get over this problem, I deeply and completely accept myself."

Or you may have to dig a bit to get to a more specific Setup: "Even though it is not safe for me to [state specific issue] ..." or "Even though I will be deprived of my favorite foods ..."

Energy Toxins

When energy toxins are the reason that EFT is not working or working slowly, it means there is a reaction on an energetic level to some part of the environment. Unlike allergic reactions that show up in our bodies, energy toxins affect the energy system and may only show up through a reversal that can stop EFT from being effective. While toxins in our environment affect us all in some way, they rarely cause a problem with tapping. In *The EFT Manual, Sixth Edition*, Gary Craig estimated that less than 5 percent of people have energy systems that are subject to substantial interference by environmental toxins.

Thus energy toxins are not a significant problem in EFT. Those who are affected by an energy toxin, however, can have massive reversals. Sometimes these reversals can be balanced long enough for a tapping sequence to work. Other times not. It is best to refer these people to a more experienced practitioner who specializes in chronic, complex cases.

Some people are sensitive to electrical "appliances" like cell phones, CD/DVD players, computers, and pagers. If you feel these affect your success with EFT, find a place to tap that is a sufficient distance from such objects. Some practitioners recommend that people with EFT effectiveness difficulties remove all jewelry and even their glasses while tapping. It won't hurt. Food is an energy toxin for some. Often the food we eat affects how we feel. It's not a stretch to see that what we eat could also affect our energy system. Sometimes simply staying away from these items will make us feel better. Sometimes the toxin itself is  actually the cause of our emotional problem. Jane, an EFTer in Atlanta, found she got nowhere in tapping on her depression until she stopped eating wheat. Terry, a next-door neighbor, was sensitive to a certain brand of toothpaste. In such cases, staying away from the substance to which you are sensitive relieves your problem.

A medically diagnosed allergy is not the same thing as a reaction to an energy toxin. Energy toxins affect the energy field. You can have a variety of medically diagnosed allergies that respond well to EFT. In dealing with allergies, use all your detective questions: When did you first notice your allergy? What was going on in your life at or just before that time?

Since the environment can, at times, influence the effectiveness of EFT, try using EFT in different locations – a different room, a different building, outside – or tap at different times of day. Perhaps the problem *is* something you ate or another toxin you were around. In these cases, it is helpful to wait a couple of days and try tapping for that issue again. Remember that *energy toxins that affect EFT are rare.* Don't be tempted to say, "Oh, EFT is not working because of an energy toxin." Dig deep for all other reasons before you give up because of an "energy toxin."

Hydration

Most practitioners have water available for their clients. This is a factor in having a welcoming environment for your client. Since water conducts electricity, it is logical to think that being dehydrated can affect EFT results. Many practitioners believe strongly that hydration makes a difference in the effectiveness of EFT. Gary Craig, however, said he does not see hydration as an issue.

Keep drinking water; it is good for you. Offer water to your client. If that changes the result – for whatever reason – great! If not, keep looking for other reasons that EFT is not working.

Skill Level of the Practitioner

As a beginner, your practitioner is usually yourself. You can learn the tapping points in just a few minutes and, if you tune in to an issue, even as a beginner, generally you can have a high level of success. It takes study and practice, however, to become really good at detective work, finding core events behind issues, and dealing with the myriad issues and complexities that can come up as you go along.

Some noncomplex issues can be dealt with quickly and simply with EFT. The need for more advanced skills shows up in an EFT session when an issue is complex, changes from simple to complex, or when the client doesn't easily connect to their issues or feelings. In skilled hands, EFT can work up to 95 percent of the time. To use EFT to its fullest potential, you will need additional study. Attend another class; rewatch EFT videos; read case studies and more; find a tapping buddy and swap EFT; get feedback. You may wish to have a session or two with a very experienced practitioner to deal with your own issues including fear of failure. Keep in mind that tapping away your fear of doing something doesn't make you good at it! Develop a self-study plan with your practitioner or tapping buddy and learn what you need to know. Fortunately, it is not necessary to know everything there is to know about EFT to begin getting impressive results.

It bears repeating, especially if you plan to work with others using EFT, to continue to work toward resolving your own issues. For a practitioner, there is no substitute for self-work. And never assume that because you have had the same issue as the client that the client is responding in the same way you did. Never assume that the "picture" in their head is the same as the "picture" in yours. Each client is an individual and their individual response to their events must be explored from their perspective – not yours. The more of your own "stuff" you've cleared, the better able you are to see clients as the individuals they are.

Test Your Knowledge

1. You or your client has the issue of "I don't trust people." What kinds of questions could you ask to find a specific event or hidden issue to tap with?

2. Which of these could slow down EFT progress?

    a. The belief that "If I let this go, I will be letting the person get away with it."

    b. Strong negative beliefs

    c. The belief that "I'm a tough case."

    d. The belief that "It's because of this that I am who I am."

    e. Not being specific.

    f. Tapping too long on one point.

    g. All of the above except f.

3. True or false? Hydration is important in EFT work.

Answers can be found in Appendix C

Personal Peace Procedure – Doing Our Own Work

The Personal Peace Procedure involves making a list of every bothersome specific event in your life and systematically using the Emotional Freedom Techniques to address each of these events one by one. Even if you are not able to resolve an issue fully, using EFT consistently is an excellent way to relax and relieve emotional distress.

Make a detailed list of all the negative events in your life that you remember. Most people have well over a hundred. Then tap on one each day. Continue until you have fully addressed all the involved aspects; some issues may take more than one day.

As you eliminate the emotional baggage, you will have less and less internal conflict. Less internal conflict translates into a higher level of personal peace and less emotional and physical suffering. For many, this procedure results in resolving lifelong issues that more traditional methods have not been able to relieve.

If you want to use EFT methods with clients, it is especially important for you to do your own work and to gain additional knowledge past level 1. Though we are never totally finished with our own issues, working regularly toward becoming aware of and resolving our own issues is a critical part of becoming a skillful EFT practitioner.

Remain Conscientious

EFT is a wonderful tool. It is a marvelous relaxation method that helps our body heal itself. It can reduce or even eliminate the emotional charge on memories of negative events. It is a simple and effective way to calm ourselves. Its simplicity can be misinterpreted as meaning that EFT can be used for anything and anybody at any time. The caveat is that, while EFT is simple, people are not!

You have just learned how to use a very powerful tool. Your enthusiasm and early successes may lead you to think you can work with anyone and anything. Though we do not wish to discourage your heartfelt enthusiasm and desire to help others, we must remind you that there are situations that need to be left to highly trained people with the knowledge and skills to deal with the complexity of serious emotional problems.

People are often much more complicated as we begin to address deeper emotional issues. We don't always realize what is going to come up until we get started on the memories. Dealing with one aspect of a problem can bring up another and another, like a magician pulling out scarf after scarf. This is a strength of EFT, but a complexity in dealing with people as some of these "scarves" can be very painful and highly emotional. These highly emotional aspects may break into the defenses of a person, resulting in the negative experience seeming to be relived in the here and now. The person can become very emotionally upset. This can be a scary event for an unprepared practitioner.

Most of us successfully compartmentalize our emotional lives from our working and social lives and have good boundaries. The boundaries between past painful life experiences and "now" are much more fragile in others. As a beginner, keep your EFT experiences to simple issues and specific definable events.

Ethics

As practitioners, we are familiar with the edict "first, do no harm." This is our first priority whenever we work with others. All licensed professions have a code of ethics covering their members. Whatever your profession as a practitioner, please review your code, as it also applies to implementing alternative techniques. There are many ethics codes written by the organizations supporting practitioners of energy-based therapies. ACEP (Association for Comprehensive Energy Psychology), AAMET (Association for the Advancement of Meridian Energy Techniques), and EFT Universe all have ethics codes on their websites. We encourage you to read and abide by the ethics code of your chosen organization. We have also mentioned several times in this training resource to practice only within your scope of practice, training, and competence. We repeat that here, but offer the following suggestions as well.

EFT is a *very* helpful technique that we believe should be in every professional's toolbox. We, the authors, however, do not consider EFT to be a stand-alone "therapy" or "treatment." When working with others, it may be hard to avoid situations involving *Diagnostic and Statistical Manual of Mental Disorders* (DSM-IV) categories. It is important, however, when you recognize you are beyond your own scope of practice, that you make an appropriate referral to someone who is qualified to deal with these types of problems. We urge you to develop several good referral sources. In addition, having a consultant or mentor is helpful.

Be aware, too, of what you "call" yourself. For instance, unless you are a psychologist, do not use the term "energy psychology" in your title. We have used the term EFT Practitioner throughout this training resource. There is currently no specific title for practitioners using energy techniques such as EFT. ACEP uses the term "energy health practitioner." AAMET uses "meridian energy practitioner." Whatever title you choose, you should be open and honest about your experience. Make sure your website and other marketing materials are descriptive of your credentials and training and where you got them.

Part of the "do no harm" dictum is to create a safe environment for any client. This includes protecting their confidentiality. If you don't already have a system for protecting client information, you should develop one. If you are a practitioner, it is important that you obtain proper informed consent to use EFT, as you would with any approach. If you decide to use EFT with others, it would be helpful to have a clear informed consent form. Keep in mind that current, laws, guidelines, rules, and regulations vary from country to country, state to state, profession to profession. Keep abreast of those that cover your chosen profession and location.

The authors would like to make it clear that, for you to train to be an EFT practitioner, much more is needed than simply reading and studying this EFT level 1 training resource. EFT is a wonderful self-help technique; however, using it with others requires training.

Try It On Everything

Some people have a hard time understanding the concept that EFT uses the same process for every issue. The questions guiding the detective work may change, and each person is certainly different, but the basic process of using EFT remains the same: get specific, tap the points, and test the results. Our medically oriented population is used to being given a different pill or treatment for each problem. People often ask some variation of this question: Will it work on this? Or, how do you do it for X? The concept that the same process could work for everything seems even more difficult to accept than the apparent strangeness of tapping on the body to fix an emotional issue.

There are hundreds of articles and testimonials written about EFT being used successfully for thousands of different issues and problems. It is the authors' intent for this training resource to give you the tools to begin your own healing. Go for it: try it on everything.

We encourage you to learn more about EFT whether through classes, DVDs, or books. We are excited for you and wish you well in your EFT journey.

Ann Adams
www.EFT4PowerPoint.com
Karin Davidson
www.HowToTap.com

Bibliography

ACEP Ethics Committee. (2009). ACEP guidelines for representing yourself as an energy practitioner. Association for Comprehensive Energy Psychology. Retrieved November 27, 2010, from www.energypsych.org

Adams, A. (2008) *Insider's Guide to Marketing Your EFT Practice*. [CD]. Media, PA: Vision Stream Studios.

Adams, A. (2009) *In Pursuit of Excellence*. [DVD]. Media, PA: Vision Stream Studios.

Adams, A. (2009) The Pursuit of Excellence. In P. Bruner & H. Bullough (Eds.), *EFT and Beyond*. (pp. 41-67). Walden, UK: Energy Publications, Ltd.

Adams, A. (2011) *EFT4PowerPoint: Your Comprehensive Training Package*. [CD]. Rome, GA: self produced.

Arenson, G. (2001). *Five Simple Steps to Emotional Healing: The Last Self-Help Book You Will Ever Need*. New York: Fireside.

Baker, A., Carrington, P., & Putilin, D. (2009). Theoretical and methodological problems in research on Emotional Freedom Techniques (EFT) and other meridian based therapies. *Psychology Journal* 6(2):34–46.

Baker, A. H., & Siegel, L. S. (2005, April). Can a 45 minute session of EFT lead to reduction of intense fear of rats, spiders and water bugs? A replication and extension of the Wells et al. (2003) laboratory study. Paper presented at the Seventh International Conference of the Association for Comprehensive Energy Psychology, Baltimore, MD.

Bandler, R., & Grinder, J. (1975a). *The Structure of Magic I: A Book About Language and Therapy*. Palo Alto, CA: Science & Behavior Books.

Bandler, R., & Grinder, J. (1975b). *The Structure of Magic II: A Book About Communication and Change*. Palo Alto, CA: Science & Behavior Books.

Barker, M., & Barker, A. (2001). *Getting Results! With Basic Meridian Technique – a self applied intervention. www.altinterventions.com*: self-published.

Brattberg, G. (2008). Self-administered EFT (Emotional Freedom Techniques) in individuals with fibromyalgia: A randomized trial. *Integrative Medicine: A Clinician's Journal*, August/September.

Callahan, R. (1985). *Five Minute Phobia Cure. Dr. Callahan's Treatment for Fears, Phobias, and Self-Sabotage*. Delaware: Enterprise Publishing.

CDC (2010). Adverse childhood experiences reported by adults - five states, 2009. Morbidity and Mortality Weekly, 59(49):1609-1613.

Church, D. (2009). Fighting the fire: Emotions, evolution, and the future of psychology. *Energy Psychology Journal* 1. Retrieved October 12, 2010, from http://energypsychologyjournal.org/?p=63

Cialdini, Robert B. (1998) *Influence: The Psychology of Persuasion*. New York: HarperCollins.

Craig, G. (2008). *The EFT Manual*. Santa Rosa, CA: Energy Psychology Press.

Craig, G. (2011). *The EFT Manual*. Elite Books.

Craig, G. (Producer). (n.d. a). *From EFT to The Palace of Possibilities: Foundational EFT* [DVD]. USA: Craig.

Craig, G. (Producer). (n.d. b). *The EFT Course, Part II* [DVD]. USA: Craig.

Craig, G. (Producer). (n.d. c). *The EFT Course: Six Days at the VA* [DVD]. USA: Craig.

Craig, G. (n.d.). Tutorial 12: The "tell the story technique": An important tool for being thorough. Retrieved October 12, 2010, from www.eftuniversity.org/tutorial/tutorltwelve.htm

Davidson, K. (2009). *Meridian Tapping Techniques: EFT Level One Training*. Media, PA: self-published.

Diamond, J. (1988). *Life-Energy Analysis: A Way to Cantillation*. Ridgefield, CT: Enhancement Books.

Dorfer, L., Moser, M., Bahr, F., *et al.* (1999). A medical report from the stone age? *Lancet* 354:1023–1025.

Doyle, R. and Look, C. (2007) *Law of Attraction and EFT*. [DVD]. USA: AttractionDVD.com

Durlacher, J. (1994). *Freedom from Fear Forever*. Arizona: Van Ness Publishing.

Eden, D. with Feinstein, D. (2008). *Energy Medicine: Balancing Your Body's Energies for Optimal Health, Joy, and Vitality*. New York, NY: Penguin Books.

Felitti, V., Anda, R., Nordenberg, D., *et al.* (1998) Relationship of childhood abuse and household dysfunction to many of the leading causes of death in adults: The Adverse Childhood Experiences (ACE) study. *American Journal of Preventive Medicine* 14:245–258.

Flint, G. A. (1999). *Emotional Freedom: Techniques for Emotional and Physical Distress*. Vernon, BC: NeoSolTerric Enterprises.

Gallo, F. (1998). *Energy Psychology: Explorations at the Interface of Energy, Cognition, Behavior, and Health*. New York: W. W. Norton.

Gallo, F. (2000). *Energy Diagnostic and Treatment Methods*. New York: W. W. Norton.

Gallo, F. (2002). *Energy Psychology in Psychotherapy*. New York: W. W. Norton.

Goodheart, G. (1991). *Applied Kinesiology*. Out of Print: Touch for Health.

Hover-Kramer, D. (2002). *Creative Energies: Integrative Energy Psychotherapy for Self-Expression and Healing*. New York: W. W. Norton.

James, W. (1884). What is an emotion? *Mind* 9:188–205.

Kendall H. O., Kendall F. P., & Wadsworth, G. (1949) *Muscles: Testing and Function*. Baltimore, MD: Williams and Wilkins.

Kenny, L. (2009). *Ultimate EFT Level 1 Workbook*. San Francisco: self-published.

Lake, D., & Wells, S. (2003). *New Energy Therapies: Rapid Change Techniques for Emotional Healing*. Inglewood, Western Australia: Waterford Publishing.

Lambrou, P., & Pratt, G. (2000). *Instant Emotional Healing: Acupressure for the Emotions*. New York: Random House.

Lynch, V., & Lynch, P. (2001). *Emotional Healing in Minutes*. London: Thorsons.

Milne, H. (1995). *The Heart of Listening*. Berkeley, CA: North Atlantic Books.

Mollon, P. (2008). *Psychoanalytic Energy Psychotherapy: Inspired by Thought Field Therapy, EFT, TAT, and Seemorg Matrix*. London: Karnac Books.

Moss, G. (2010). *Level 1* [Handout]. Ilkley England: self-published

Nader, K., & Hardt, O. (2009). A single standard for memory: the case for reconsolidation. *Nature Reviews Neuroscience* 10(3):224–234.

Rowe, J. (2005). The effects of EFT on long-term psychological symptoms. *Counseling and Clinical Psychology* 2(3):104–111.

Salas, M. M., Brooks, A., Rowe, J. E., & Church, D. A. (2009). The effect of an energy psychology intervention (EFT) versus diaphragmatic breathing on specific phobias. Paper submitted to the *Journal of Clinical Psychology* for peer review.

Scaer, R. (2006). The precarious present. *Psychotherapy Networker* 67:49–53.

Sidney, S., Sise, M. T., & Bender, P. (2007). *The Energy of Belief: Psychology's Power Tools to Focus Intention and Release Blocking Beliefs*. Santa Rosa, CA: Elite Books.

Wells, S., Polglase, K., Andrews, H., Carrington, P., & Baker, A. (2003). Evaluation of a meridian-based intervention, Emotional Freedom Techniques (EFT), for reducing specific phobias of small animals. *Journal of Clinical Psychology* 59(9):943–966.

Wolpe, J. (1969). *The Practice of Behavior Therapy*. New York: Pergamon Press.

EFT Practitioners mentioned in this training resource:

Adams, Ann	www.EFT4PowerPoint.com
Beer, Sue	www.theEFTcentre.com
Carrington, Patricia	www.MasteringEFT.com
Davidson, Karin	www.HowToTap.com
Freedom, John	www.JohnFreedom.com
Kenny, Lindsay	www.LifeCoachingwithLindsay.com
Look, Carol	www.AttractingAbundance.com
Lynch, Paul	www.The-Heart-Centre.com
MacKay, David	www.EFTmx.com
Moss, Gwyneth	www.Emotional-Health.co.uk
Roberts, Emma	www.theEFTcentre.com
Sise, Mary	www.IntegrativePsy.com

Appendix A –
EFT Workshop Exercises

These exercises were adapted from Gwyneth Moss's implementation of Gary Craig's original workshop guidelines. These exercises can be conducted in pairs or in threes (one member in the role of observer). Time should be left at the end of the exercise for questions and to process what occurred during the exercise.

Exercise 1: Emotional Response to TV/Film/Novel

This exercise is designed to help you learn to identify a specific scene, to practice developing a Setup from the specific statement on that specific scene, to stay focused, to measure the intensity of the scene, to utilize the Basic Recipe (shortcut) EFT points, and to test the results after tapping.

Break up into pairs. Pick which partner will be first to bring to mind a single scene or short sequence from a fictional film or a novel. Pick any scene that brings up emotional intensity as you think about it. Ask your partner to tell you in just a few words what happens in that scene: the coffin lid moved on its own, he's trapped by the Dalek, Bambi's mother died, the hand came from nowhere, the people falling off the Titanic, they are surrounded by snakes. Such a brief description is all you need to know. You do not need them to tell you what film it is, the whole story, or why the scene gives rise to emotional intensity.

Keep your partner focused on the one specific scene they described. Ask your partner to rate on the 0-to-10 scale the intensity of the feelings or emotions they are experiencing *now* as they focus on the scene. They do not need to name the emotions or feelings; just keep them focused on how they currently feel about the one scene. Tap a round of the Basic Recipe (shortcut) using the name of the scene as the Reminder Phrase.

Basic Recipe: H – Top of head (optional point that some practitioners use as the last point rather than the first); EB – Eyebrow; SE – Side of Eye; UE – Under the Eye; UN – Under the Nose; Ch – Chin (under the lower lip, in the crease); CB – Collarbone; UA – Under the Arm.

1. Tap on the Karate Chop point, or rub the Sore Spot, as they say the Setup three times, "Even though [their description, such as, the coffin lid moved on its own] I truly and deeply accept myself."
2. Use the shortcut points (Basic Recipe) and the Reminder Phrase until the intensity of the memory name drops to a low level.
3. Test the current intensity by asking them to bring the scene to mind again and to notice with what thoughts, feelings, or body sensations they may have. Ask what the intensity is now and what is different about the scene.
4. Repeat the previous steps using the new definition of the scene to form the Setup and Reminder Phrase.
5. Retest. If the intensity is down to 0, swap roles and repeat the exercise. If not, repeat the previous steps again.

Make a brief record of the information on this chart: the issue addressed, the results of testing the intensity, and any notes you might have.

Issue addressed:

Original SUD:

After first round:

Ending SUD:

Observer notes:

Exercise 2: Emotional Response to a Trigger, or What Pushes *Your* Buttons

This exercise shows that even small issues can create significant intensity and perhaps lead to other aspects of the problem. It gives you practice at assessing intensity, creating a Setup, tapping the points, and testing the results.

Break into pairs. Ask your partner to describe a specific everyday situation (no matter how trivial) that triggers an emotional or bodily response out of proportion to what is happening. For example:

- intense anger when made to wait on the phone
- anxious impatience in the checkout line
- feeling nervous when having to speak to a group or give a report
- someone taking up two spots in a parking lot
- feeling fear in the presence of a tiny mouse
- major reaction to the dishwasher not loaded correctly

Clarify the scene by asking your partner to think about the situation and to notice the thoughts, feelings, and body sensations that arise. Ask them to rate on a scale of 0 to 10 the intensity of their emotional response to the event. Choose a few of their exact words to create the Setup that seems to best describe the situation.

Basic Recipe (shortcut): H – Top of Head (some practitioners use this point as the last point rather than the first); EB – Eyebrow; SE – Side of Eye; UE – Under the Eye; UN – Under the Nose; Ch – Chin (under the lower lip, in the crease); CB – Collarbone; UA – Under the Arm.

1. Tap on the Karate Chop point, or rub the Sore Spot, saying the chosen Setup three times: "Even though I feel small when the boss looks at me ..." "Even though I feel frustrated and tense when I can't get through on the phone ..."
2. Tap the Basic Recipe (the shortcut points) with a Reminder Phrase formed from their words. Do at least two rounds.
3. Test by asking about the intensity as they now think about the situation.
4. If it is not down to a 0, do two more rounds, adding in the word "remaining" to the existing Setup. Or if they have shifted to another aspect or part of the situation, use their words to form a new Setup and Reminder Phrase and tap the EFT points.
5. When their intensity is down to 0, swap roles and repeat the exercise.

Issue addressed:

Original SUD:

After first round:

Ending SUD:

Observer notes:

Exercise 3: Emotional Response to a Bothersome Memory

By now you should be clear on the EFT process of identifying a specific issue and creating a Setup and Reminder Phrase, as well as the importance of testing. In this exercise, you will use the Full Basic Recipe with all the points and the 9 Gamut Procedure. You will also practice the Tell the Story Technique and using the last few words your partner says in the story for the next Setup.

Ask your partner if there is something that happened in the past that as they think about it, the memory brings up an emotional intensity *now*. Respect that you and your partner are beginners at EFT and stay clear of major traumatic events. Pick a memory that may seem embarrassing, like your sister reading your diary in front of her friends or being shouted at by a teacher or the time you came out of the bathroom at work with your skirt tucked into the back of your underwear or your zipper not zipped.

Ask them to give the event a simple name and to say that name out loud. Ask for a measure of emotional intensity as they say that name. Begin by using the name of the memory in the Setup and Reminder Phrase: "Even though I have this embarrassing Mrs. Bloodworth memory, I truly and deeply accept myself."

Full Basic Recipe: H – Top of head (some practitioners use this point as the last point rather than the first); EB – Eyebrow; SE – Side of Eye; UE – Under the Eye; UN – Under the Nose; Ch – Chin (under the lower lip, in the crease); CB – Collarbone; UA – Under the Arm; BN – Located an inch Below the Nipple; Th – Thumb; IF – Index Finger; MF – Middle Finger; BF – Baby Finger; KC – Karate Chop point.

Now add the 9 Gamut Procedure. Remember to tap the Gamut point continuously as you hold your head level and look straight ahead while performing the following actions: close your eyes; open your eyes; look hard down right to the floor; look hard down left to the floor; imagine a very large clock on the wall and roll your eyes as if you are looking at each number in order; roll your eyes in a circle in the opposite direction; hum about two seconds of any song or melody; count from one to five very fast; hum about two seconds of any song or melody again. Go back through the tapping points.

Check the intensity; if 4 or below, move on to asking them to tell the full story of what happened. Remind them they may keep any private bits to themselves. If at any time they feel *any* emotional intensity, or you notice they are becoming intense, remind them to stop. Create a Setup and tap. Continue to tap for any intense part of the story. Use the last phrase or few words they used as the Setup: "Even though Mrs. Bloodworth shouted at me when the boys laughed ..." After tapping for each intense part of the story, have them retell the story and tap for any remaining intensity until they have no more intensity on that part. When you have worked through the entire event, test by asking them to retell the entire story.

Issue addressed:

Original SUD:

After first round:

Ending SUD:

Observer notes:

Exercise 4: Addressing Physical Symptoms

For this exercise, you will ask permission to tap *on* the other person. You will discover how it is different to tap on someone, or to be tapped on. You will recognize the importance of asking if they have been medically evaluated. You will become aware of the variety of ways that someone can describe their pain or physical symptom. You may also notice that the pain or symptom moves around in the body.

Before tapping on another person, *always* ask permission. So be sure you do that with your partner, even if you know them. When dealing with any physical issue, remember that, as a practitioner, if you are not a medical doctor, you need to ask the client if he or she has seen a doctor to have the problem evaluated. Never give medical advice or make medical recommendations.

Ask your partner if there is pain or a physical sensation or a physical appearance to the symptom. Ask your partner to describe how it feels or looks or how else they experience the symptom.

They may give a description as *literal* as: "This hot, sharp pain just in my mid back." Or it may be a more *metaphorical* description, such as: "This Mississippi mud pool in my knee." Or *like a character:* "This breathing dragon in my right shoulder." You can tap for the *medical diagnosis:* "Even though I have increased fluid pressure and resulting hardening of my eyeball called glaucoma ..." Or you may choose first to address the *feelings or emotions about the symptom:* "Even though I am so angry that my knee is letting me down ..." Or the *implicit emotion:* "Even though this pain is really angry at something or somebody ..." Or the *personal feelings* about the physical issue: "Even though I am afraid I can't play golf ..." Or "Even though I feel totally stupid for missing the chair ..."

6. Ask your partner to rate the intensity on whichever description or emotion as it is now on the 0-to-10 scale.
7. Create a Setup from their description of or emotion around the physical symptom.
8. Tap on your partner for several rounds using your choice of the Basic Recipe (shortcut) or the Full Basic Recipe.
9. Check back in with your partner as to what is coming up for them now. Listen carefully, observe what is happening. Notice if the pain moved or symptom changed in any way. Use their responses to modify or create new Setups.

Repeat the tapping sequences and follow what comes up.

Issue addressed:

Original SUD:

After first round:

Ending SUD:

Observer notes:

Appendix B –
Powerful EFT Questions

In his sessions, Gary Craig used many questions to help people tune in to their issue and to find the core issue. Probing questions such as the ones listed here, gathered from Gary Craig and dozens of other practitioners, are important in the detective work to get to the core issue. But all the right questions won't help unless you *have a true sense of curiosity* about your client. All truly successful practitioners have a well-developed sense of curiosity and wonder. The following "detective" questions are given as an example of the kinds of questions that gather important information about yourself or your client. Obviously, they would be used in the context of the client's story.

How do you know that?

How do you know you do not know?

What makes you think that?

Who told you that?

Who/what does that remind you of in your life?

Who do I remind you of?

Why did you pick that reaction?

If there were an emotional component to the pain, what would it be?

If this pain had a name, what would it be?

If you did know, what would it be? Just guess. Make it up.

If your friend had that pain, what would it be?

If there were an emotional contributor to this problem, what would it be?
What was going on in your life when this started?

What would _____ say about that?

What/who is to blame for that?

What was your first thought after the incident?

Who did you tell about this? How did they respond?

Who did you hope would never find out?

Did you have a sense something was wrong before this happened?

Did someone say dreadful things to you that you replay to yourself now?

What's your theory about this problem (or pain)?

How would you describe this?

What details do you see when you think about this?

If you could live your life over, what pivotal event or person would you eliminate?

What would you do to change that?

Did something occur in your life in the last year?

What happens when you try?

What does that mean?

What do you want to happen?

Teach me how you do that.

An example of that would be_____?

How do you know you are not worthy/lovable/etc.?

What do you do to make that happen?

Where do you feel that?

What sets that off?

Who taught you that?

What reason could he have had for doing that?
What does _____ mean to you?

What do you get out of keeping that behavior/belief/issue?

What will you lose if you stop that behavior/belief/issue?

What do you have to think about to feel like that?

When (or where, or with whom) does it happen worst?

And then what happens?

Is there anything you don't think you could possibly get over?

If there were another issue we haven't yet identified, what would it be?

What is your biggest issue now?

What is still bothering you about _____ right now?

What does this issue/person remind you of?

When was the first time you remember feeling this way?

Can you give an example of how this problem affects your life?

And what else bothers you about this?

If there were a deeper emotion underlying this problem, what might it be?

If your pain had a face, what would it look like?

How does having this problem make you feel?

If there were a reason not to get well, what would it be?

What was happening in your life before or when this happened?

Who wants you to get better? Who doesn't?

What is your greatest fear about this pain?

Is there a message this pain is telling you?

If there were a reason to keep this pain, what would it be?

What's the upside of keeping this problem?

What's the downside of giving up this problem?
When you become stuck on an issue, ask yourself:
    What's in the way here?
    What have I not yet seen?
    What core issue have I been unable to find?

Gary Craig also often used paradoxical statements:

I wouldn't want to make you think you could be flexible.

Even though I am not completely over this issue, *yet* …

Exaggerate the grandiosity of their belief: "Even though *nobody* else in the world feels this way …"

Buttons being pushed is an inside job.

You are a prisoner of his words.

We all have handwriting on the wall; we and others put it there.

Appendix C – Answers to "Test Your Knowledge"

1. Children cannot be taught EFT. False

2. EFT can be performed by
c. anyone who is willing to learn it

3. What "bridge" would you use to describe EFT? Possible answers include:

EFT is like hypnotherapy but adds extra power to the process because it integrates the body's subtle energies and it integrates beautifully with hypnotherapy because it allows us to take the process even deeper.

EFT is like talk therapy with the advantage that it allows us to get to the issues faster and resolve them more thoroughly.

EFT enhances massage therapy by adding an important emotional relaxation process.

EFT blends perfectly with Cognitive Behavioral Therapy because it helps bring up the issues faster and creates more (and deeper) Cognitive Shifts behind the scenes.

EFT is like Systematic Desensitization except that it is much gentler and often faster.

EFT enhances our Chiropractic work because it allows us to include important emotional issues and to integrate the body's subtle energies.

EFT is a technique for BEHAVIORAL DESENSITIZATION; i.e. the example of Pavlov's dogs.

PAGE 25

1. What is the "Discovery Statement?"
The Discovery Statement says that negative emotions are caused by an energy disruption. Energy disruptions happen when we have a negative thought. This disruption can be seen as a "clog" in our energy system. We clear the clog by tapping on the meridian points while focusing on the bothersome issue. Tapping sends pulsing through the meridian and therein "fixes" the energy disruption. Energy flows freely again and the negative emotion is neutralized. Tapping while focusing on the negative emotion clears the disruption.

2. EFT holds that a person's_____ causes negative emotions.
c. thoughts about negative experiences

3. True or False? Generally speaking, EFT tends to work slower than traditional therapy. False

4. True or False? When something happens now, our subconscious minds look in the past for a way to react. True

PAGE 29

1. The Karate Chop point is located _____.
b. at the flesh side of the hand below the little finger

2. Where are the other "Basic Recipe" points located on the body?
Eyebrow Point (EB)
Side of the Eye Point (SE)
Under the Eye Point (UE)
Under the Nose Point (UN)
Chin Point (Ch)
Collarbone Point (CB)
Under Arm Point (UA)
Top of Head (H)

3. True or false? You must tap using the fingers of your dominant hand.
False

PAGE 36

1. List the four parts of the EFT process.
The Clarification, The Setup, The Tapping, The Testing

2. Describe each part of the EFT process.

The clarification - Develop a specific description of your issue, preferably a specific event, and rate the associated intensity from 0 – 10.

The setup - A specific statement (example) of your stated problem, along with your acceptance of yourself in spite of the problem.

The tapping - Tap about seven times on each point while repeating your Reminder Phrase.

    EB – Beginning of eyebrow
    SE – Side of the eye
    UE – Under the eye
    UN – Under the Nose
    Ch – Chin
    CB – Collarbone
    UA – Under Arm
    H   – Top of Head, or Crown Point.

3. The first step of the EFT process involves taking a_____ issue and making it a _____ issue.

b. global/specific

4. Briefly describe the Sore Spot.

The Sore Spot is about where you would pin a medal or place a name tag. To find it, put your fingers in the "u" at your throat; go down a couple of inches, then across about four inches to either side. You will find a sport that is tender to the touch.

PAGE 41

1. Briefly explain in your own words why in EFT we focus on the problem (the "negative.") Answers may be similar to:

You are recognizing and accepting what is going on right now for you, *your truth* – at this moment in time – you are accepting how *you really feel* deep inside.

2. An essential component of the EFT Setup is to

b. accept that you have a problem.

3. True or False? It is important for people to add in a statement of how they think they should feel. False

4. What may a person do if they are not comfortable with the acceptance statement?

Acceptance statements may be modified. *Any* statement can be used that shows acceptance for how you truly feel.

5. True or false? Focusing on the positive is the best way to use eft successfully. False

1. True or False? It is possible to have an emotion without a corresponding physical reaction. False

2. What is SUD?
SUD stands for Subjective Units of Distress and a 0-10 scale used to rate intensity of emotion.

3. The cause of all negative emotions is
a. disruption in the body's energy system

1. True or False? Beginners should start with more complex issues rather than simpler ones. False

2. Explain the importance of "Getting Specific."
The goal is to isolate specific events that led to developing the fear, belief, or conclusion I developed around the presenting problem. These specific events help shape the truths I feel about myself. Until we resolve the feelings that arise from specific events, we cannot change our emotional response. Specific events usually yield quicker outcomes with EFT.

3. What are the general detective questions you can ask to encourage specificity?
Who, What, When, Where, & How (Stay away from Why so we don't get defensive)

4. When tapping, if you become suddenly emotional, it is important to
c. keep tapping.

1. Most issues have_____.
c. many aspects.

2. Explain the concept of "Daisy Chains."

During EFT, you may shift to another aspect of the same issue, or you can jump to another related issue. The daisy chain effect is an opportunity to address multiple aspects in one session.

3. True or False? The more layers an issue has – the more complicated it is to resolve it. True

PAGE 58

1. In your own words, describe "aspects."
Aspects are like the puzzle pieces of a larger problem. There can be many pieces to the problem.

2. The point of tapping on phobias is to give you_____.
b. a choice.

3. True or False? New aspects can appear while tapping. True

PAGE 62

1. True or False? It is important to describe your physical response to an emotion as accurately as possible. True

2. The metaphor of the "forest" and the "trees" explains _____.
b. the Generalization Effect.

3. According to Gary Craig, what is the biggest mistake that new EFT students can make?
According to Gary Craig, the biggest mistake that new EFT students can make *is attempting to use EFT on issues that are too large, complex, or global. New EFTers may be able to make progress on a global issue if they are persistent, but, if this takes a long time, they may give up too quickly.*

PAGE 72

1. What is the purpose of The Movie Technique?
The movie technique allows you to focus on the specifics and details of your issue. If you can't make a movie of your issue, your issue is too global for EFT to work effectively.

2. Clients will always go directly to the specific issue. False

3. When working with a client's story it is important to
c. tap until the intensity level is significantly diminished.

PAGE 77

---

1. The client must have a big emotional charge for EFT to be effective.
False

2. Doing my own EFT work is important because_____.
The more you have worked through your own issues the calmer you can respond to another's issues. The more you have done your own work the less you are "triggered" by your client's stories.

3. If your client (or you when working on your own issues) becomes very emotional, you would
d. remain calm and keep tapping until the emotions regulate.

PAGE 85

---

1. Find a physical issue in your own body (past or present) and clarify it using the techniques you have just learned. Write it out in detail.
Clarify your physical issue using some of the following:
 Clarifying the Pain
 Physical Descriptions
 Emotional Reactions
 Related thoughts and/or traumatic events
 COLOR OF PAIN

2. What questions would you not ask in working with physical issues?
c. What do you need to do to increase the pain so we can focus on it?

PAGE 89

---

1. Describe borrowing benefits.
Borrowing Benefits is decreasing the intensity on your own issue as you tap along while watching a session where another person is working on their issue.

2. In building rapport with your client, which of the following is unimportant?
c. Hairstyle

3. There is only one way to measure intensity. False

1. What is the importance of having the client find the first time they remember the feeling?
Resolving the client's earlier issues can resolve the more recent issues faster.

2. Small events are usually not significant. False

3. Testing in vivo means
a. doing the very behavior that was problematic before the EFT session.

1. How can EFT address cravings?
EFT addresses cravings by giving you (or the client) the option of a choice.

2. Select the best time to tap for a craving.
a. when thinking about the substance

3. There is no difference between a craving and an addiction. False

1. The 3 basic steps in the Basic Recipe and the Full Basic Recipe are different. False. The 3 basic steps are:
The Clarification
The Setup
The Tapping

2. The 9 Gamut was developed to balance extreme emotions. (True or False)
False. The 9 Gamut was developed as a brain balancing exercise to balance the left and right hemispheres of the brain.

3. What are the steps in the 9 Gamut procedure?
1. Close your eyes
2. Open your eyes
3. Look hard down right to the floor while still holding your head straight ahead

4. Look hard down left to the floor while sill holding your head straight ahead
5. Roll your eyes in a circle. Imagine a very large clock on the wall and you are looking at each number in order
6. Roll your eyes in a circle in the opposite direction, look at each number in the opposite order
7. Hum about two seconds of any song or melody
8. Count from one to five
9. Hum about two seconds of any song or melody again

PAGE 110

1. The easiest way to address reversals is to
d. use the Setup.

2. Three reasons EFT may appear not to work could be missing aspects, not being specific enough, and lack of persistence. True

3. Working on your own issues helps you become a better EFT practitioner. **True**

PAGE 115

1. You or your client has the issue of "I don't trust people." What kinds of questions could you ask to find a specific event or hidden issue to tap with?

Do you remember a time when you DID trust people? When did it change?

How does not trusting people make you feel? Where in your body? When is the first time you can remember feeling that same feeling in your body?

Think back and try to remember the first person you didn't trust. What was going on?

2. Which of these could slow down EFT progress?
g. All of the above except f.

3. Once I'm good enough at EFT, I don't have to work on myself anymore.
False

CPSIA information can be obtained
at www.ICGtesting.com
Printed in the USA
BVOW09s1213010318
509333BV00004B/165/P